SUBMARINE

TECHNOLOGY

Model
SUBMARINE
TECHNOLOGY

BY NORBERT BRÜGGEN

© Auflage 1993 by Verlag für Technik und Handwerk
Postfach 1128, 7570 Baden-Baden
English Language © 1996 Traplet Publications Limited
Translated from the original German by Keith Thomas B.Sc.
Technical Support by Nick Burge

Published by Traplet Publications Limited 1996
Traplet House,
Severn Drive,
Upton-upon-Severn,
Worcestershire. WR8 0JL
United Kingdom.

ISBN 1 900371 04 9

Front Cover
German Type 23 U-boats were produced in 1944, most being destroyed but two survived until 1965.
This model was scratch built by Steve Warner, and the underwater photo was taken by Nick Burge.
Cover designed by Steaven Heppener.

Back Cover
This photo shows the typical layout of a modern model submarine, the body moulded in GRP sections
covering a space frame which is self supporting and contains all the working parts.

Technical drawings by Lee Wisedale

T R A P L E T
P U B L I C A T I O N S

Printed and bound by Stephens & George Limited,
Merthyr Industrial Estate, Dowlais, Merthyr Tydfil, Mid Glamorgan CF48 2TD

Foreword

Over the last few years interest in boat modelling has been growing steadily, and the specialised areas in particular are becoming ever more popular. The increasing number of submarines and working scale sailing boats seen in many regions are clear evidence of this.

Model boat kits undoubtedly have their place, and justifiably provide an easy entry route into the maritime sphere. The number of people now building model boats from kits is very large, and from amongst this group we find an increasing number of modellers who go on to discover the true creative core of the hobby for themselves. These are the folk who turn away from ready-made ideas and their implementations, and instead turn to their own imagination and personal yearnings, searching for the vessels of their dreams, now that they are within their technical capabilities. They are no longer satisfied with the conventional run of yachts, tugs and racing boats, and find themselves leaning more and more towards those vessels which most strongly embody man's dreams of distant and unknown worlds. Amongst them are old sailing ships tanned by wind and weather, and the submarines which rise mysteriously from the uncharted depths.

Unfortunately the submarine is one type of model about which there is a serious shortage of knowledge. Submarines may be "dream ships" for many, but they are technically extremely demanding and therefore difficult to "bring off". Literature discussing the problems specific to that rare species, the model submarine, is sparse and difficult to find. Until now the modeller's only recourse has been to study model boat magazines – assuming that he had the time to riffle through 10 years' worth of three different titles [applies to Germany only]. We have done just that, and have dug up many useful snippets of information such as methods of making your hatches watertight, but the fundamental problems concerning hull strength and manoeuvring capability are rarely mentioned. Until now every would-be model submariner had to do his own pioneering work.

It is precisely this fundamental information which I have attempted to set out in this book. To a large extent I have omitted detailed working instructions since in any case most modellers enjoy working out their own methods to suit their technical abilities and facilities. This is a deliberate ploy, as I feel that too much detail would rob the modeller of the need to exercise his own creative gifts.

To some extent I have used engineering terminology and mathematical formulae to express the vital inter-relationships within a successful submarine in terms of the laws of physics, as this enables the modeller to calculate the characteristics of his project extremely accurately before he starts building. Not everyone will want to work this way; however, for those who do not trust their instincts and gut feelings at the design stage the maths may well be useful. Tables showing the basic relationships are also included, designed to help the modeller who is used to using a little maths and a lot of "eyeball".

My thanks go to everyone who has helped me, especially:

- Lothar Menz for proof-reading the contents,
- Ursula Brüggen for orthographic proof-reading,
- Helmut Huhn and Gerold Schnebbe for their many years of advice,
- Rudi Jacobs for his development work on servo electronics,
- The composite fibre materials department of IKV, for the use of their computers, and my girl-friend for her moral support and considerable patience.
- To all my readers I wish success with your own designs, and hope your sub always surfaces "turret up".

Leverkusen, March 1991
Norbert Brüggen

Contents

Chapter 1

Selecting the Model

Full-size prototypes

There was a time when many a submarine modeller began his career after watching the film "Das Boot" (The Boat). Here was a fascinating underwater monster that just cried out to be modelled. This spontaneous enthusiasm would soon be overtaken by doubts when the modeller spent a little time considering: what a lot of equipment would have to be made or bought; what a lot of constructional problems there were; what a lot of money it would cost. The project would usually settle gently on a high shelf in the workshop. Until . . . that's right, until a kit of "Das Boot" turned up in the model shop.

We know of at least one case where a modeller stricken with just this infection lost no time in laying down the keel of his scale model. The thing was actually built, and there it stood, completed, on the North bank of the Maas river to the West of Rotterdam. Alas, nothing more was heard of it after its launch.

Just like flying, which has excited designers, adventurers and novel writers for ever and a day, there can be no doubt that underwater travel exerts an immense fascination on many people. In the sailing ship era – and that's not so long ago even now – the ocean depths were a place of horror teeming with fantastic sea monsters. Even though these wild ideas were subsequently put firmly in their place by the findings of scientific research, the fascination of these entirely foreign realms remains undimmed. If we wish to explore the underwater world and travel through it in a state of apparent weightlessness, we only have two options: the diver's breathing apparatus, and the submarine.

With very few exceptions however, man's attempts to invade the submarine world have been entirely with belligerent purpose. It was not until the 1960's that explorers were motivated sufficiently by the mystery of the seas to build special diving boats with research in mind. Since that time the exploitation of submarine mineral sources has developed into a commercial undertaking, and now represents a large and extensive branch of industry.

Even so, it is films such as "Das Boot", "Unternehmen Petticoat" (Exercise Petticoat) (incidentally: have you every seen a pink "Gato"?) and numerous similar efforts that are mainly responsible for the popular image of the submarine. In fact, to many people the type VIIc U-boat is simply "the" submarine, and as a result it is the type most often modelled. The vast literature concerning the Second World War has also played its part here, as the subject of submarines is an important one in that context. Many submarine modellers think of little more than the boats of this time, although there are a few who discuss modern military subs.

The last World War was certainly an important period in the history of submarines, and undoubtedly it is only right that many models should be made of these vessels, but even so there is a drastic imbalance! There have been many other boats which are very interesting, both before and after the 2nd World War. Here are a few of the well-known ones:

Brandtaucher (Fire Diver) (built 1850)

This represents one of the most important and inventive efforts in the sphere of submarine construction, as it

A model of the "Brandtaucher", built for film purposes

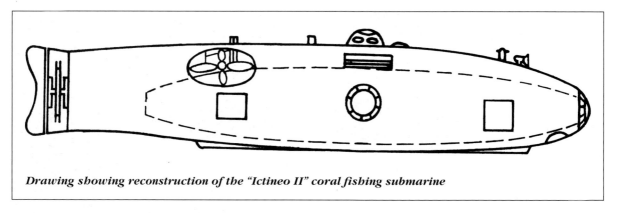

Drawing showing reconstruction of the "Ictineo II" coral fishing submarine

was the first vessel to incorporate the solutions to all the problems of submarine travel. The diving tanks were intended to take the form of piston tanks, but lack of funds prevented their inclusion. An adjustable spindle-mounted trim weight provided the means of inclining the boat, and a screw operated by treadwheels provided forward thrust. An interesting feature is that the boat relied upon ballast water and trim weight for control, i.e. it had no hydroplanes.

Numerous documents concerning this boat are extant, and the original vessel is exhibited in the Dresden army museum. This "sea monster" makes a very primitive-looking model. Its successor, the "Seeteufel" (Sea Devil), gives a similar impression, although in this case more trust was placed in the designer and the vessel actually made successful runs.

Ictineo 2 (built 1866)

This submarine was built in Spain for the purpose of coral fishing. The designer, Narciso Monturiol, was the first to make a systematic study of the strength of the pressure vessel required, and as a result his boat was of double-skin construction with a cylindrical pressure hull.

The materials he used were olive wood and oak because of their superior working qualities, and the whole was clad in thin copper sheet to provide a water-tight seal. The boat had observation windows at the bow and sides and also featured external implements which could be operated from inside the hull, which we would call "manipulators" today. Again the boat had no hydroplanes, instead relying on side-mounted propellers for manoeuvring.

The streamlined external shape endows the vessel with a very modern appearance, and it could be expected to have very acceptable manoeuvring characteristics. The unusual materials would also help to produce an interesting model.

Nautilus (devised 1870)

Jules Verne was a masterful author who was able to write gripping stories based on the ideas, predictions and inventions of his contemporaries. For his book "20,000 leagues under the sea" it seems likely that he combined the most propitious ideas of the time and rolled them into the fictitious Nautilus submarine with its electric power system

I know of two versions of this boat:

The drawings accompanying the first complete edition of his works show a spindle-shaped submarine with a smooth outer skin and no control surfaces. It features an extending control stand.

In contrast the version made for the Walt Disney film is of bizarre and monstrous fish-like form, in which the requirements of the dramatic scenario were evidently more important than matters of streamlining and technology. The result is a prototype for a model which is bound to be the centre of attention wherever it appears – surely a good thing. Since it is an imaginary vessel in any case, the modeller can let his imagination rip with an easy conscience.

The "Nautilus" (here based on Walt Disney's ideas) responds to the command "dive" for the first time ever

Holland No. 1 (built 1901, England)

John Phillip Holland was a teacher of Irish descent who lived in America, and he succeeded very early on in making military submarines which actually worked. The USA and England both purchased several of his vessels, and many countries bought boats or plans from Holland as the starting point for their own program of submarine development. His company, the Electric Boat Company, still exists today, building American atomic submarines.

The original Holland submarines were all of similar design with a hull of plump, clumsy teardrop shape, a propeller and cruciform rudder at the stern and a very small superstructure. For surface running the boats were set with the bow inclined up by 5°, to keep the deck out of the water and the propeller reliably in it.

In November 1913 one of these boats sank in a storm when on tow

"H.M. Submarine Holland No. 1" built by a Belgian modeller, surface-running in a canal

to a scrapyard. This was fortunate for us because in 1981 it was located by a minesweeper and subsequently raised and restored. Today it can be viewed in the Royal Navy Submarine Museum at Gosport. A plan is also available.

German submarines (built 1914/15)

We can consider these as representatives of many other bizarre types built in the first World War. They are small, simple coastal submarines displacing only 140 tonnes, and their three sections could be transported by rail. The bulky shape of two foreshortened cones and a cylinder is immediately obvious. They were of simple construction and used existing items of equipment, and this allowed each boat to be completed in the sensationally short time of 100 days. In spite of their small size these boats were capable of an amazing duration at sea. In respect of their construction, which was designed for fast manufacture above all, they can be considered the direct predecessor of the type VIIc, and as such are of great historical significance.

English R-class (built 1918)

These are probably the most curious submarines to see action in the first World War. Built as part of an emergency programme during the war, these vessels were fitted with an internal combustion engine system producing a mere 250bhp, coupled with small fuel tanks. The true capabilities of these sub-hunter submarines were only evident when submerged. Although only displacing 500tons the vessels' 1000bhp electric motors gave them an underwater speed of 15kn, which is still a respectable value today. Large control surfaces made them highly manoeuvrable, and they were also fitted with a sonar system to help them locate their target. This again was an innovation at the time.

In general terms foreign submarines are almost unknown to German modellers, and I find this very sad as there are many interesting designs amongst them.

Adventurous projects from the 2nd World War

These projects include the miniature submarine "Delfin" (dolphin), a teardrop shaped one-man submarine with cycle power system, although the first prototype had an electric motor. The highly efficient hull shape gave the sub a speed of 17kn from a mere 32 horsepower. This level of performance was a big surprise to maritime experts, especially since the vessel was designed by a coachbuilder. A diving cell was not included, as the vessel's speed made it possible to dive dynamically without any difficulty.

The efficient hull form also endows the model with a good turn of speed (e.g. 9.9km/hr from 36 Watts of electrical power in a 1:10 scale model). These are measured values for the model shown here, which has given its builder quite a lot of fun in trial runs.

Even simpler in shape was the miniature submarine "Schwertwal" (narwhal), and it too was extremely fast, this time due the enormous power of the Walter turbine which powered it. It represents a good prototype for a simple beginner's model based on a length of ready-made pipe. Of course, the technical problems would be much more severe if you were to aim for scale speed.

The most unusual project known to us went under the name of "Manta", and was a very fast miniature submarine with an 800 horsepower Walter turbine for power. A submerged speed of 30kn was claimed, and as

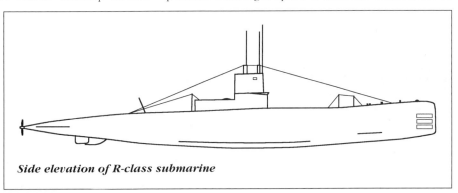

Side elevation of R-class submarine

"Delfin" from Bremen. An easily managed model of the "Delfin" to 1:10 scale, incorporating dynamic diving, like the full-size

much as 50kn when planing on the surface! Flight was the only claim not made for this vessel. Even if this sounds somewhat improbable, something like it in model form should be possible as we have plenty of powerful electric motors available.

"Soucoup Plongeant" by Jaques Cousteau

There can be few people who do not remember the

A semi-scale model based on Jaques Cousteau's "SP300". Only displacing 400g, this little model dives and surfaces in an aquarium

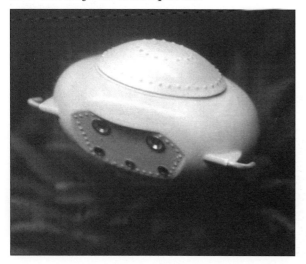

films made by Cousteau during his scientific research dives in the "Calypso". His "diving saucers" – that is what the name means in English – played an essential role in his success, as they were able to penetrate to depths out of reach of divers. They were developed in the period 1951 – 1959 specifically for this purpose, since the only research submarines built until then – the bathyscaphes (such as the "Trieste") were too large and clumsy for the task.

The elliptical pressure hull has space for two persons. The submarine is manoeuvred by means of two swivelling water jets, a ballast trimming system (moving a weight to tilt the boat) and the diving cell. All the apparatus is arranged in a belt around the pressure hull, giving the submarine its characteristic shape.

An original example is on view in the Oceanic Science Museum of Monaco.

"Alvin" (built 1964)

This famous American submarine also dates from the early period of research vessels. Like most submarines of its type it is designed for optimum manoeuvring capability at very low speeds (1kn). It is fitted with a number of viewing windows and a manipulator to cope with tasks close to the seabed.

It has been used successfully for many years, but only recently it was employed in locating the "Titanic", providing spectacular pictures and excellent material for headline writers.

Unusually for a research boat its external form is smooth and harmoniously shaped.

Penguin B3

This is the name given to an unmanned mine-sweeping drone which was produced by MBB. Its purpose is to detect mines on the seabed under cable control from a mothership. It then places a small bomb next to the mine, which is detonated later to remove the mine. The vessel is equipped with sonar and a TV camera. Two power pods and a propeller [two propellers?] provide its manoeuvring capability.

In spite of its military purpose, the "Penguin" minesweeping drone is painted fluorescent orange

Fish

When searching for prototypes there is no real need to keep to the underwater inventions of man's mind. Nature offers a rich fund of ideas for us to plunder.

All fish and whales are propelled by means of fin strokes, and this method is by no means inefficient as the dolphin paradox shows: these animals have been clocked at speeds of 45km/hr, and it has been calculated that it would need to produce more than 20 horsepower to reach such speeds if it were operating at the efficiency typical of a man-made submarine. However, the dolphin's muscle mass only gives it the capability to produce 2 horsepower, and only then for short periods.

If we attempt to emulate this fishy form of propulsion using mechanical apparatus we can probably get nowhere near these extremely impressive values, but on the other hand the power we have at our disposal is relatively large.

The mechanical means of producing fin strokes actually consists of no more than an eccentric and a pair of levers, although difficulties would certainly arise in controlling such a system. However, that is surely where the real fun is to be found in modelling.

Model making usually boils down to the miniaturisation of a given technical design; however, it can also be an obsessive concern to create something completely new. Think of the early period of aviation: without modelling there would probably never have been aircraft, since all the knowledge gathered by the pioneers was gained from models in the first instance.

Nautilus

There have been numerous submarines bearing this name, but the original cephalopod, related to the squid family, has been in existence for millions of years. Stone fossils of their spiral-shaped calcium shells are extremely common, but living examples do exist, and can be seen in large aquaria. They move by ejecting a jet of water backwards, and this should present no great technical problem to the modeller. The hard shell would also be straightforward to reproduce.

Foot rowing crab [lit. cyclops]

This crab, also known as the little hopper moves forward by jerking its very large pair of antennae backwards. Just imagine a monster 10:1 scale crab 20cm long, jerking its way across the model lake with powerful strokes!

The types mentioned here are by no means comprehensive, as the animals and machines which could be taken as model prototypes are simply innumerable. However, I hope that they might give you an idea or two about your next project. As the photographs show, some of these suggestions have already been taken up, but others are waiting for you. It would be wonderful if the model scene could be enlivened a little with some colourful and inventive new models. As things stand

All too often sharks are associated with notions of anxiety and fear, but surely the idea of modelling such a harmonious propulsion system is a magnificent challenge?

This Nautilus, photographed in the Dusseldorf Aquazoo, is a living fossil

practitioners of this highly individual hobby tend to emulate what has already been done rather than trusting their own ideas.

Where to operate your model submarine

When you are considering the construction of a new model submarine you are likely to be guided primarily by your personal preference and taste. However, there is more to it than that, and this applies to submarines in particular.

A vital aspect of your selection process is the stretch of water in which you intend submerging your model. If you are looking for the optimum boating lake, this is what you should seek:

- Crystal-clear water with a surface like a mirror, so that you can observe your model distinctly even when it is 10m down.
- A jetty reaching out into the middle of the lake giving you a good view at all times, and allowing you to position yourself so that you are not blinded by the sun's reflection in the water's surface.
- A bottom devoid of weed, because that's where the propeller will inevitably get tangled up otherwise.
- A bottom devoid of mud, to avoid the embarrassment of your boat burying itself completely in soft slime when you make a hash of controlling the hydroplanes.
- A bottom of contrasting colour to your submarine, i.e. in most cases as light as possible. Even better: a light-coloured boat over a dark bottom.
- Water of ultra-low electrical conductivity, so that the radio waves can penetrate to the boat.
- A bottom located exactly at your model's maximum diving depth. This excludes the possibility of damage to the pressure hull, but at the same time gives you maximum freedom of movement.
- A team of willing and experienced divers permanently on call, preferably in the water, in case something unexpected happens.

Where on Earth do we find anything like that?

Models of research submarines (this is one of the TOURS range) gives loads of fun combined with good visual contact

In fact, a swimming pool comes very close. The only major limitation is the permeability of the water to radio waves, which gives us an effective depth of no more than 3.5m at best. If the water is 4m deep at the diving board end we will need a suitable safety circuit – or a diver. For initial trials – until the submarine has shown real signs of reliability in its basic functions – I strongly recommend that you find a super-safe stretch of water such as a swimming pool. Unfortunately it can be rather difficult to get permission to use them for model submarine trials. Public pools are always in use, and private pools are few and far between. But you never know; perhaps a friendly pool manager will feel inclined to co-operate once you have shown him your finished model.

Open-air ponds and lakes are usually extremely cloudy, although this does vary with the type of pool and the season of the year. Muddy waters are generally unpleasant to use – more or less so depending on the type of submarine – but they are unfortunately true to life and therefore "scale". Even in the open ocean the visual range under water is seldom greater than one boat's length.

Research submarines are always outstandingly manoeuvrable, and here good visibility is very important otherwise you quickly lose track of what you are doing. Once you lose control you may as well surface and stay there. Unfortunately all the the fun of three-dimensional movement is lost if you stay on the surface.

Murky water is even more troublesome if you have installed a still or video camera in your submarine. The range of horizontal vision under water is always less than you estimate from the surface. To make effective use of a camera you really need to take your model to a mountain lake or – the simpler solution – wait for the Winter, as cold weather prevents the growth of micro-organisms which cause the cloudiness of the water in the first place.

In the narrow sense of the term a submarine is designed exclusively for under-water running, and only surfaces in an emergency or when there is no alternative. A good example of this is the atomic submarine. The dominant operating mode of these vessels is running at constant depth – generally with the assistance of a depth regulator – at moderate to high speeds (5 – 10km/hr). Models of such machines should ideally be run submerged at a known depth – ideally just at the limit of vision – so that the operator always knows where his boat is, but spectators and other modellers quickly lose track of it. Even in completely obscure water an experienced submarine operator can still follow the course of his boat by its wake. The wake is visible even when the submarine is completely submerged, provided that it is not too deep and maintaining a fair speed.

Submarines classed as diving boats – i.e. vessels which normally travel on the surface and only dive in an emergency, such as the type VIIc U-boat – can operate happily in murky waters, as the scale mode of operation is to run on the surface and only carry out short diving manoeuvres. If visual contact is lost you can always bring the sub back to the surface again. Naturally it is possible to run such a vessel like a pure submarine, maintaining a shallow submerged depth with the help of a depth regulator, perhaps at periscope depth, but in this case the lack of speed means that no visible wake will be produced.

The other factor which has to be considered in the choice of prototype is your own manual capabilities and technical facilities (lathe, milling machine and so on). This is particularly true of model submarine construction since the task is that much more exacting than the building of a surface vessel.

Many minor constructional problems can be solved easily and more elegantly with a lathe, but that does not mean that it is impossible to make an efficient, reliable submarine without this tool. Admittedly it may require considerable manual ability and good improvisational skills to solve a given problem with ordinary hand-tools and the materials which you happen to have (i.e. cheaply). However, this is only a hobby, and we don't always need to compare our products with those of our colleagues and competitors. Far more important is the modeller's personal satisfaction and the feeling of success which he experiences. I have much greater admiration for the imaginatively designed model submarine competently built using a fretsaw and a kitchen knife, than for the high-tech monster sub which could not have been constructed without the help of a CNC milling machine. Even scrap materials can be pressed into service to make a working model submarine that will give you hours of fun. Anyway, who ever said that a model has to look like a full-size prototype?

In this book I present a number of designs which can be constructed with simple means, as well as the complicated, more elegant solutions.

The French builder of these fantasy boats, from scrap plastic materials, christens them "Moustique Furieux" and "Poseidon"

Chapter 2

Design

Mass, buoyancy

The reason why boats float and submarines are capable of staying motionless under water, in an apparently weightless state, was discovered by Archimedes more than 2200 years ago: a submerged body produces buoyancy equal to the weight of water which it displaces. If the submerged body is to remain at a fixed depth, its buoyancy must be exactly the same as its own weight. If this is the case, the body is in a state of equilibrium and stays at its present depth. If the submarine is any lighter – just a few grammes is all it takes – then it will rise to the surface. Once at the surface a small part of the boat's volume projects out of the water, and the vessel's buoyancy diminishes to the point where it is the same as the boat's weight. If the submarine is any heavier than the water it displaces, then it will sink to the bottom.

If this equilibrium of forces is present, then it is present at any depth since neither the boat nor the water alter their characteristics with depth. You might expect that the submarine would sink naturally to a particular depth and stay there, as water density is greater lower down, so giving more upthrust. In fact this situation rarely arises, and only then as a result of differences in temperature or salinity.

If we want stable equilibrium for our model submarine, we have to create it. This is done by adjusting the vessel's buoyancy by means of the diving cell or by creating artificial control forces by means of deflecting the hydroplanes. Both measures require the operator to observe the sub's depth constantly, and make adjustments as necessary to compensate for unwanted deviations. When the operator is standing on dry land this is a difficult task, as his depth perception is quite poor from this standpoint. The alternative is to install an automatic depth regulator which controls the hydroplanes or the diving cell. In this way the boat can be made to stay at one depth, and this is the preferred and recommended method.

In the real world this state of equilibrium is not a stable one, since the submarine itself is compressible whereas water is not; at greater depth water pressure increases and the boat becomes slightly smaller. If we assume that the vessel is in equilibrium at a particular depth and is then made to dive, the water pressure acting upon it rises and the hull is compressed. If the volume of the hull falls, then it displaces less water, and its buoyancy diminishes. Gravity takes over, and the boat sinks at an ever increasing rate.

The opposite case is where the boat is at a higher level than the equilibrium depth. Buoyancy increases, and the boat rises faster and faster. Since our model submarines are all relatively "soft" (see "pressure hull strength") this effect occurs even at the shallow depths with which we are concerned. Air is particularly compressible, and this applies to the air in a partly flooded diving cell. The air provides buoyancy, but it is also subject to external pressure. Keeping such a boat at a constant depth – i.e. at equilibrium – is a difficult enterprise which requires very fine corrective skills. This is an inherent disadvantage of using air under external pressure as a means of providing buoyancy, and right at the initial design stage it is best to avoid using this system. If that is not possible – an example might be a compressed air diving system without a separate regulating cell – it is best to use as small an air bubble as possible in order to minimise this unwanted effect.

When a submarine is running on the surface a stable state of equilibrium exists, as the hull only displaces as much water as it itself weighs. The rest of the hull

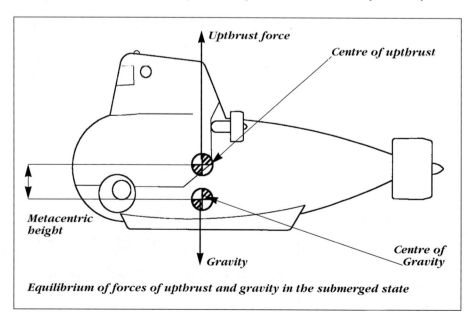

Equilibrium of forces of upthrust and gravity in the submerged state

Labels in figure: *Upthrust force*, *Centre of upthrust*, *Metacentric height*, *Gravity*, *Centre of Gravity*

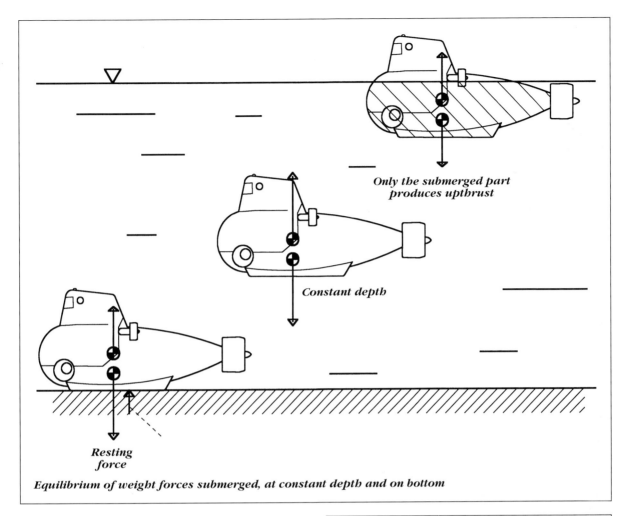

Only the submerged part produces upthrust

Constant depth

Resting force

Equilibrium of weight forces submerged, at constant depth and on bottom

projects above the surface and produces no upthrust. If the boat becomes partially submerged, e.g. when striking a wave, the displaced volume immediately rises, buoyancy rises in proportion, and the boat rises back to its original position.

The floating characteristics of surface vessels are very good-natured, and if this is the limit of your experience you may well find it difficult to become accustomed to the sub's very sensitive behaviour when submerged. From the initial planning stage it is vital to keep a very close eye on the model's total weight. While a small amount of excess weight in a surface vessel just results in a slightly lower waterline, the same would render a submarine useless, as it would simply sink to the bottom and stay there.

It therefore makes obvious sense to consider submerged running as the more critical phase of running, and to leave the boat's surface running characteristics to look after themselves. In fact, if the boat dives well, it will float well too.

The likely weight of your model submarine can be found relatively easily just be weighing the component parts and adding the weights together. You can simply refer to the manufacturer's catalogue for the weight of radio control units, batteries and motors, or just weigh them yourself. The weight of the hull you are about to build is naturally much more difficult to predict.

If you have already built a similar boat you can make an estimate of the new vessel's hull weight based on the

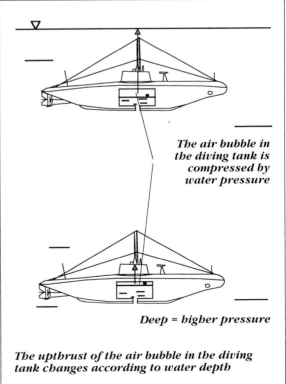

The air bubble in the diving tank is compressed by water pressure

Deep = higher pressure

The upthrust of the air bubble in the diving tank changes according to water depth

existing one. If it is an entirely new project, all you can do is calculate the hull weight based on the surface area, thickness and density of the proposed hull material. You should then add a generous amount to allow for all the sundry equipment such as cables, fixings, hydroplane installation, rudder system and linkages etc.; this can easily add another kilogram. Finally you should add a safety margin to allow for everything which turns out heavier than you planned. In this way you should be able to ensure that your estimate turns out on the safe side. This is important; after all, you can always add ballast to the finished boat, but there is hardly ever an opportunity to remove weight.

The easiest and most accurate method of establishing the buoyancy of your boat is to complete the hull and carry out flotation trials. This means placing the model in the filled bathtub or some other body of water and adding ballast until the boat just floats. Remove the whole thing and weigh it.

At the planning stage, i.e. before the hull actually exists, all you can do is attempt to calculate these values, but this is still useful and valid. A good starting point, although extremely approximate, is to use the water displacement of the full size vessel in its submerged state, and convert that figure:

Model displacement = original displacement scale.

If we take the submarine which is most often modelled – the type VIIc/41 U-boat – and a scale of 1:40, the result is as follows:

$$860\text{m}^3 \times (1{:}40)\text{m}^3 = 0.01344\text{m}^3 = 13.44\text{dm}^3$$

Please note that the volume of the flooding compartments inside the model, and certain other details, will not be exactly in proportion to those of the full-size vessel, so this value should only be used with care.

A much more accurate method is to break down the hull into cylinders and cones which approximate to its shape, and then calculate their volume. The basic rule here is to err on the small side, i.e. select a volume for calculation which is slightly smaller than the real hull section. In this way you will again be on the safe side in your figures.

The diving cell volume required is determined by the displacement of those components of the boat which are intended to be above the surface when the vessel is floating. These parts no longer displace water, and therefore produce no upthrust; the weight of the contents of the diving cell compensates for this. The volume of the vessel which is above the surface can be calculated using the same method used to find the hull volume.

It is helpful if this volume is not too large, and this can be achieved by building the turret and deck as free-flooding areas.

This means that these sub-assemblies are provided with holes through which water can flow and fill the void as far as the pressure hull. They therefore displace no water and produce no upthrust. Similarly no power is required to raise them out of the water since the water simply flows out again.

In fact these parts do displace a little water in so far as the thickness of their material gives them volume. The material does not need to be very strong, so thin sheet metal is the obvious choice, combining sufficient strength with small volume.

Certain submarines such as the Polish "Orzel" were fitted with diving cells constituting one third of the boat's volume. Models of such prototypes can only have a realistic appearance on the surface if they are built with large free flooding areas. At the other end of the scale are research boats and atomic submarines, of which only a very small part protrudes above the surface, since they are designed purely for submerged running. As a result their diving tanks can be quite small. All that is required is a regulating cell with sufficient volume to allow depth control and manoeuvring. Its maximum upthrust only has to compensate for the loss of

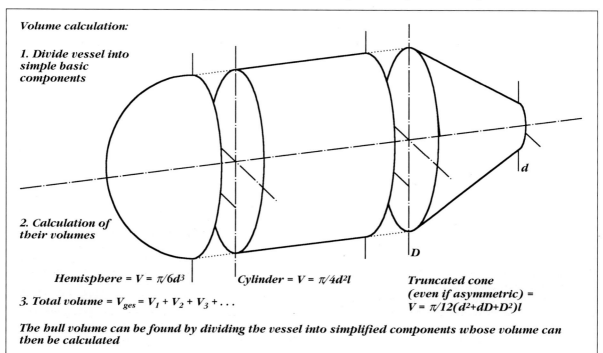

Volume calculation:

1. Divide vessel into simple basic components

2. Calculation of their volumes

Hemisphere = $V = \pi/6d^3$ Cylinder = $V = \pi/4d^2l$ Truncated cone (even if asymmetric) = $V = \pi/12(d^2+dD+D^2)l$

3. Total volume = $V_{ges} = V_1 + V_2 + V_3 + \ldots$

The hull volume can be found by dividing the vessel into simplified components whose volume can then be calculated

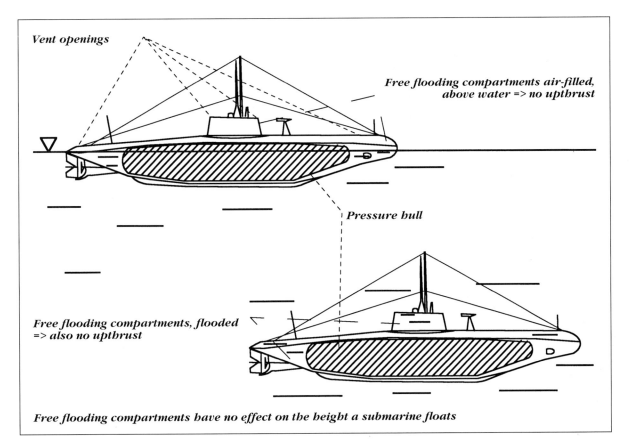

Vent openings

Free flooding compartments air-filled, above water => no upthrust

Pressure hull

Free flooding compartments, flooded => also no upthrust

Free flooding compartments have no effect on the height a submarine floats

hull volume due to outside pressure. For models this only needs to be one to two percent of the boat's volume.

As already mentioned, only a few grammes of weight either side of neutral are required for surfacing and diving. In my experience it is best to balance the model in such a way that it remains at a constant depth when the regulating cell is 80% flooded. This ensures that a slight amount of downthrust can be produced on the one hand, while plenty of upthrust is available for an emergency. The rates of rise and fall can be calculated as follows:

$$V_{vert} = \sqrt{\frac{2 \times F_{vert}}{ro \times c_w \times A}}$$

where

V_{vert}: vertical speed in m/s
F_{vert}: vertical force in N
ro: density of water = 1000kg/m³
c_w: coefficient of drag under vertical movement (approximately circular cylinder l/d = 10) = 0.82
A: wetted surface (width x length) in m²

For example, the rise speed of a class 206 model to a scale of 1:50 with a 100cm³ regulatory cell is:

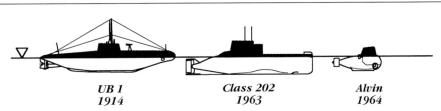

UB 1 1914   **Class 202 1963**   **Alvin 1964**

The silhouettes of the profiles of three different submarine types show the varying volumes above water, and the large difference in diving cell volume required

$$\sqrt{\frac{2 \times 0.8N}{1000kg/m^3 \times 0.82(0.96 \times 0.096)m^2}} = 0.15m/s$$

At this speed the submarine would surface from a depth of 1m in about 7 seconds. The submerged model submarine takes slightly less time, but this is not a surprise because we have only used estimated values for c_w and A.

The point of these calculations is not to determine exact values, but to gain some coarse idea of how the vessel will behave once it is completed.

For example, it matters not one jot if surfacing takes 7 seconds or 5 seconds, but if the calculated figure is 0.5 or 70 seconds, then something is wrong and needs to be corrected.

This calculation also shows us the submarine's sensitivity to variations when at a constant depth. The same boat with an excess weight of only one gramme sinks at a speed of:

$$\sqrt{\frac{2\times0.01\text{N}}{1000\text{kg}/\text{m}^3\times0.82(0.96\times0.096)\text{m}^2}}=0.016\text{m}/\text{s},$$

which means that it dives at the rate of one metre every 60 seconds!

Static and dynamic diving

Static diving is the process of submerging with the help of a diving cell and a regulatory cell, i.e. by altering the vessel's weight, whilst dynamic diving is the process of submerging without making any such changes. The boat is balanced so that it floats with a residual buoyancy of 1-2%.

When you wish to submerge, dynamic forces are applied to overcome this buoyancy, i.e. by deflecting the hydroplanes and/or the hull forward, or by the appropriate direction of propeller thrust. Naturally this can only work if the boat is moving at an adequate speed. With models displacing around 5kg I have found that the minimum speed is about 5km/hr, but diving is easier if the speed is around 7km/hr.

The response of such boats to depth control commands when moving at full speed is exactly the same as that of the static diving boat. However, at low speeds the boat will surface of its own accord, since the dynamic downthrust is no longer sufficient to overcome the vessel's residual buoyancy. This means that boats with dynamic diving cannot be manoeuvred slowly in a small space when submerged; they must be kept running at speed. High speed under-water running can present considerable problems, and for this type of boat it is highly advisable to install an attitude regulator or depth regulator.

Some full-size submarines have also been equipped for dynamic diving. Representatives of this group are the small weapons "Delphin" and "Schwertwal" which have already been mentioned, both of which attained very high speeds for their size.

An entirely different method of producing dynamic downthrust is to use a vertical thrust propeller. This is a popular feature of research submarines, where a vertical propeller endows the vessel with extreme three-dimensional manoeuvring capability, as the sub can move vertically up and down without forward motion as well as stay at a constant depth. The control characteristics of this type of vessel are drastically different from a boat with dynamic high-speed diving, and the difference is as dramatic as that between a fixed-wing aircraft and a helicopter.

Although most research submarines use vertical thrust propellers as a means of reinforcing the effect of the diving cells, other examples exist which have no tanks at all, such as the "Penguin" (see: "Prototypes").

In high-speed submarines – including those whose only method of submerging is by hydroplane deflection – the arrangement of the hydroplanes has an important influence on the vessel's depth control characteristics. If the sub only has one pair of hydroplanes, there are two alternative locations:

a) Bow hydroplanes, i.e. planes located significantly forward of the hull mid-point, produce downthrust immediately when they are deflected downwards. The boat dives at once.

As the point at which the force acts lies in front of the Centre of Gravity, the bow also tilts downward. The angled hull now also produces downthrust, in fact to a greater extent than the hydroplanes themselves in most circumstances. However, this effect is considerably delayed due to the inertia of the boat's mass. When the hydroplanes are returned to the neutral position it also takes some while for the hull to return to horizontal.

b) With stern-mounted hydroplanes the boat's response is much more complex. The deflected planes initially produce upthrust, with the result that the hull moves up instead of down. After a time the whole boat tips forward, and this movement produces the desired downthrust. How far the boat tilts (i.e. the angle through which it inclines in the fore-and-aft direction) is determined by the force of the hydroplanes, i.e. by the angle of the planes and the boat's speed, and also by the self-righting moment which is a function

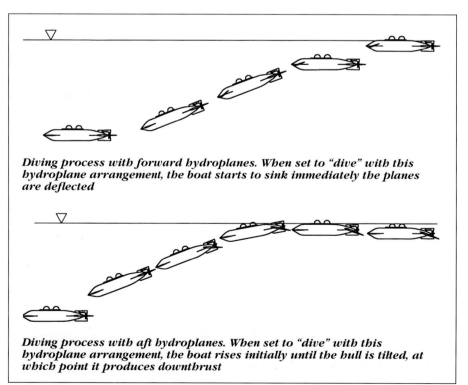

Diving process with forward hydroplanes. When set to "dive" with this hydroplane arrangement, the boat starts to sink immediately the planes are deflected

Diving process with aft hydroplanes. When set to "dive" with this hydroplane arrangement, the boat rises initially until the hull is tilted, at which point it produces downthrust

of the vessel's inherent weight stability. At low speed the possible angle of inclination is slight and the downthrust that can be achieved is correspondingly small. The same applies to a submarine which is excessively stable.

For every boat with this hydroplane arrangement there is a critical speed at which the force of

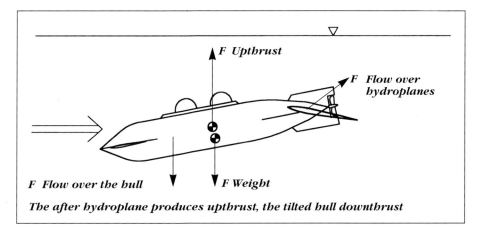

F Upthrust

F Flow over hydroplanes

F Flow over the hull

F Weight

The after hydroplane produces upthrust, the tilted hull downthrust

the hydroplanes and the downthrust produced by the resultant angled attitude of the hull cancel each other out exactly. At this speed the submarine does not respond at all to hydroplane commands. Normally this speed is low, and is easily be avoided. Either you speed up slightly and normal control is regained, or you slow down slightly and make allowance for the fact that hydroplane response will be reversed. This occurs because at very low speed only the direct force of the hydroplane has any effect, and as we have seen this works in the wrong direction. At very low speeds the inclination of the hull has no effect.

It must be clear that the indirect control characteristics of stern-mounted hydroplanes are bound to present problems to the operator. An automatic depth regulator is the obvious answer, but unfortunately it is also more difficult to make such a system work well with stern hydroplanes, as they require much more accurate adjustment than a boat with bow hydroplanes.

Mass distribution, stability

The position of the Centre of Gravity and of the Centre of Buoyancy determines the attitude of the submerged boat and its capacity to right itself.

The centre of buoyancy is the centre of gravity of the displaced water, and represents the point through which the upthrust force acts if we consider this to be a point force. In reality the boat's buoyancy is distributed over the entire vessel, but this is only important when it comes to calculating the vessel's strength.

Gravity can also be

considered as a point force acting at the centre of gravity. If the boat is in a state of static equilibrium, then the centre of buoyancy is vertically above the centre of gravity. If the boat has any another attitude, e.g. some angle of heel, then this arrangement produces a self-righting moment.

An interesting point is that this self-righting moment is of equal magnitude in the lateral and longitudinal directions in the case of a submarine, since it is purely a function of the distance between the two centres, known as the metacentric height.

When the submarine is running on the surface the relationships are more complex, as parts of the hull rise out of the water when the vessel heels, and others are submerged, and this causes the position of the centre of buoyancy to alter constantly. As a result the vessel's stability is much greater. Since for a given angle the hull volumes which rise and fall are much greater

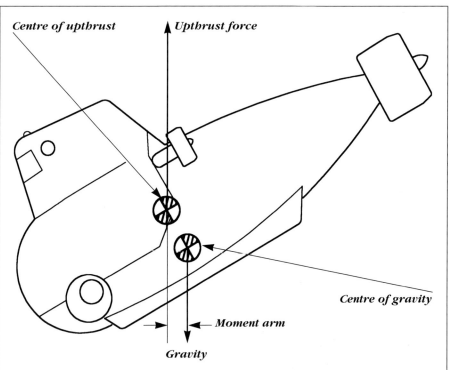

Centre of upthrust

Upthrust force

Centre of gravity

Moment arm

Gravity

Upthrust and Centre of Gravity vertically above each other at equilibrium. If this is not the case, a self-righting moment is present

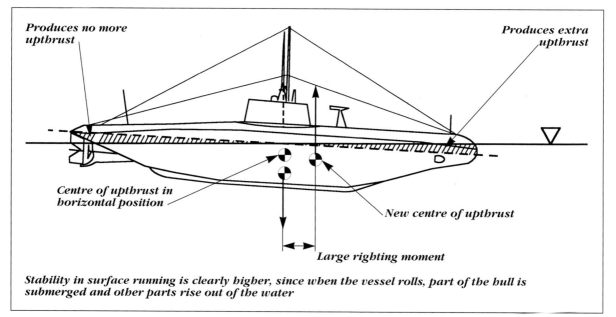

Produces no more upthrust

Produces extra upthrust

Centre of upthrust in horizontal position

New centre of upthrust

Large righting moment

Stability in surface running is clearly higher, since when the vessel rolls, part of the hull is submerged and other parts rise out of the water

longitudinally than laterally, fore-and-aft stability is much higher than lateral stability. In a submarine this makes the reduction in stability when submerged much more noticeable in the longitudinal direction than than in the lateral direction.

During the design phase of a model submarine project it is possible to select the centre of gravity and thus the metacentric height relatively freely; it therefore makes sense to consider what can and should be achieved with this freedom.

A large metacentric height results in great inherent stability, i.e. after heeling, the boat returns very quickly and strongly to its horizontal rest position. The boat is much less responsive to the rolling moment of the propeller which is always present with a single-screw power system.

Unfortunately there is a drawback to this: the boat becomes much less responsive to control surface forces, and if stern hydroplanes are the sole control method, serious problems can arise. Under the influence of the hydroplane forces the hull only inclines slightly, and the desired angled attitude can only be achieved by running the sub at high speed. It is therefore necessary to find a compromise; ideally the unwanted roll caused by propeller torque will be held within reasonable limits (a few degrees), while the hydroplanes will remain capable of tilting the boat at low speeds. On the other hand, if your submarine is fitted with a vertical thrust propeller, you can design in as high a level of weight stability as you wish, and thereby obtain a boat which is very easy to control.

If the metacentric height is small, the boat's natural tendency to return to the straight and level will be slight. Stern hydroplanes then work outstandingly well, but the boat's propeller may tip the boat on its side or even cause it to rotate. A twin-screw power system with contra-rotating propellers minimises this danger, as the torque effects largely cancel each other out. This solution allows the construction of a submarine with low weight stability which responds well to the hydroplanes at low speeds.

The extreme case is a vessel with zero weight stability, i.e. in which the centres of upthrust and of gravity

are coincident. This vessel will be stable in any position and attitude – for example, standing vertically on its nose or on its back, until new control commands are sent to move it. This represents the maximum possible in terms of manoeuvring capability, although a boat of this type requires considerable skill from its operator to keep the vessel in the desired attitude.

The position of the two centres is calculated in similar fashion to the volume and weight, i.e. by calculating the values for separate parts of the vessel and adding them together. This time however you have to calculate the moment arms (lever lengths) relating to the reference point which you have selected.

In practice the metacentric height is generally very small. Depending on the size of the boat it is usually in the range 0 to a few cm. The longitudinal centre of gravity is very critical, and a variation of just 1mm causes considerable deviations. The pitch-axis and roll-axis angles can be calculated using the following formula:

$$\alpha = \arctan \frac{A}{MZH}$$

where

α: Angle in degrees
A: Horizontal distance in mm
MZH: Metacentric height = vertical distance in mm

If the metacentric height is 10mm (approximately normal), a horizontal deviation of only 1mm produces an angle of 5.7 degrees in the boat's attitude! It is therefore clear that the completed boat must be balanced with great care.

The arrangement of the diving cell is also critical in view of the submarine's sensitivity to centre of gravity shifts. It should be installed as accurately as possible at the centre of gravity, so that the CG position does not alter when the vessel's weight changes.

One method of dealing with this problem is to arrange two diving cells forward and aft of the centre of gravity. However, this does present additional problems in ensuring that the two cells flood and empty at exactly the same rate, otherwise the boat would continually be out of balance. A single diving cell located at the CG is much easier to control, and with careful use of space it is not necessarily any more obstructive in terms of access to other internal sub-assemblies.

It is also possible to install the diving tank offset slightly towards the bow. The boat can be trimmed out to a horizontal attitude when submerged, but the boat is slightly stern-heavy when on the surface. This helps to ensure good hydroplane response during the surfacing manoeuvre and provides more stable surface running.

Of course, it is possible to control the sub by deliberately shifting the centre of gravity. A suitable weight trimming system can be produced by placing the heaviest component – the drive battery – on a slide, operated by a powerful servo.

This solution avoids the necessity of balancing the boat exactly, and also gives some extra control when the boat is static and at low speed, when the hydroplanes have no effect.

The experimentally-minded modeller might like to consider a further possibility: moving a weight laterally or vertically. Moving the weight sideways will make the vessel roll (perhaps to compensate for propeller torque) while moving the weight up or down alters the boat's metacentric height and thus its stability. You could then have a submarine which was extremely manoeuvrable when required, but could exploit the advantages of weight stability for the rest of the time.

Finally we have to mention another, unintentional, form of weight shifting, this time with extremely unpleasant results. This occurs if your sub has a diving tank with an exposed water surface. If the boat tips forward or aft, you suddenly have a problem. For example, if the boat inclines bow-down, then the water in the partially-filled tank will run towards the bow and thereby amplify the pitching movement. If the tank is excessively large or long this effect may build up to the point where the boat becomes unstable and stands vertically on its nose.

If you are of a mathematical bent you can consider this effect as a reduction in metacentric height. The most critical case would be where the surface of the water in the diving tank touches neither the bottom nor the top of the tank. For small pitch-axis angles the reduction in metacentric height is:

$$VMZH = \frac{ro \times B \times L^3}{12 \times m_{ges}}$$

where
VMZH: Reduction in metacentric height in m
ro: Density of water, 1000kg/m³
B: Width of diving tank in m
L: Length of diving tank in m
m_{ges}: Total weight of boat in kg

$$MZH_{ges} = MZH_{excl\ tank} - VMHZ$$

If the resultant metacentric height $MZH_{ges} = 0$, the boat's weight stability becomes zero or even negative, and the vessel is then unstable.

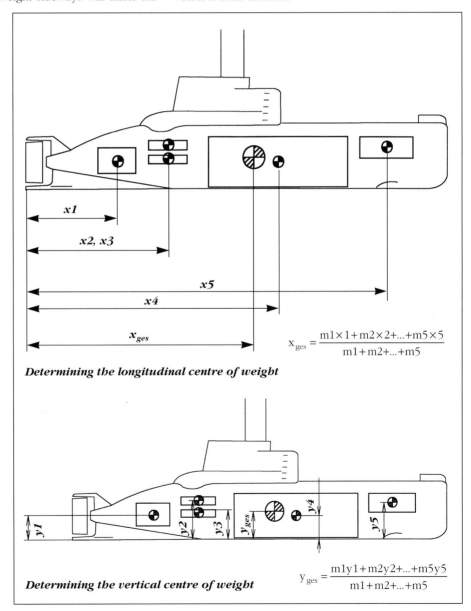

$$x_{ges} = \frac{m1 \times 1 + m2 \times 2 + ... + m5 \times 5}{m1 + m2 + ... + m5}$$

Determining the longitudinal centre of weight

$$y_{ges} = \frac{m1y1 + m2y2 + ... + m5y5}{m1 + m2 + ... + m5}$$

Determining the vertical centre of weight

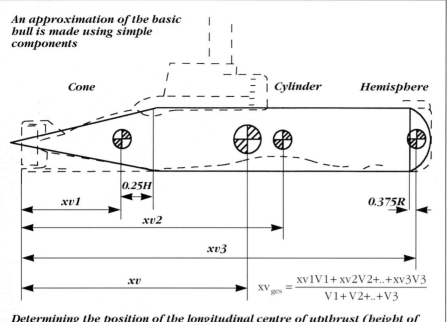

An approximation of the basic hull is made using simple components

Cone   Cylinder   Hemisphere

0.25H

xv1

xv2

xv3

xv

0.375R

$$XV_{ges} = \frac{xv1\,V1 + xv2\,V2 + .. + xv3\,V3}{V1 + V2 + .. + V3}$$

Determining the position of the longitudinal centre of upthrust (height of Centre of Gravity found using method similar to that used for determining position of the Centre of Gravity)

The formula shows that the length of the tank is much more important that its width, since that value is cubed in the calculation, while the basic width value is used directly. It is therefore clearly advantageous to keep the tank as short as possible. The type VIIc U-boat and other similar submarines used saddle tanks, but these are completely unsuitable for our application.

Drive systems, propellers

Unfortunately many modellers immediately think of "slow" when they think of "scale", although in fact just as many modellers err in the opposite direction, and run their models much too fast.

I once built a "V80" experimental submarine to 1:30 scale and sent it hurtling through the water at 9km/hr, and my esteemed modelling friends furrowed their brows.

They took a lot of convincing that this is indeed the scale speed, and not, as one might have expected, 1km/hr. The calculation is relatively simple:

$$V_{mod} = \frac{V_{org}}{\sqrt{Ma\beta stab}}$$

U5 with central diving tank. Removing the outer hull sleeves shows the arrangement of the diving cell close to the Centre of Gravity

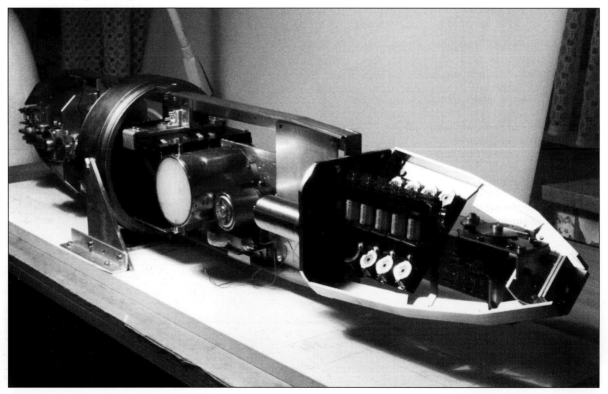

Many years ago a Mr. Froude discovered that a model boat moving at the speed calculated by this formula set up wave formations which were similar to that of the full-size, and in the same way the wave resistance converts correctly.

Once a submarine is in its proper element – i.e. fully submerged – we do not need to trouble ourselves with wave formation. Under water the boat's running resistance is not determined by the waves, but only by the vessel's wetted surface area. Even so, Froude's law is still valid. The boat's control characteristics are critically determined by its speed of control response, and it is precisely the magnitude of these oscillation processes at model scale which this law defines.

Therefore if model submarine manoeuvres are to look realistic we should never forget old Mr. Froude and the time scale which is the outcome of his law. For example, movie films look "right" when they are recorded at accelerated speed, according to the appropriate time scale, and are then shown in slow-motion so that the spectator can see the event converted back to low speed.

If we want our boat to run at the appropriate scale speed we naturally need to know how much power is required. For a submerged submarine this is extremely simple to calculate using the "admiralty constant". This constant defines the speed which a ship can attain with a given shaft power. It takes into account the vessel's water resistance and propeller efficiency, and is largely independent of the size of the vessel.

$$C_b$$
$$= \frac{D[t]^{0.66} \times v[kn]^3}{P_b[KW]}$$
$$= \frac{D[kg]^{0.66} \times v[km/h]^3}{P_b[W]} \times 1.574$$
$$= \frac{D[t]^{0.66} \times v[kn]^3}{P_b[PS]} \times 1.359$$

where

c_b:	Admiralty constant
D:	Water displacement
v:	Speed
P_b:	Power at the shaft, units stated as in [ ]

The admiralty constant can thus be calculated if we have the data pertaining to the original full-size vessel. However, since water does not flow so efficiently round models, and small-scale propellers are never as efficient as full-size ones, a "model factor" of 1.5 to 2.0 has to be included in the calculation. The average value here is 1.75.

If we study the steadily rising values it is clear how the design of streamlined shapes has advanced over the years. The differences between model and full-size are harder to analyse. In the case of the "Class 206" submarine the model exhibits an extremely good emulation of the vessel's propulsion characteristics, with the result that the model achieves the same excellent admiralty constant as the full-size vessel once we apply the model factor which we have already mentioned. The same applies to the "Walter V80" experimental boat, although the values themselves are inevitable lower, despite the fact that they were outstandingly good for the time.

With the Type XXI the model's propulsion system did not work out so well, and the difference is considerable.

A power servo moves the main drive battery through +/- 10mm, thereby altering the attitude of the submarine by +/- 30°

In the case of the Forelle (an experimental boat dating from 1902) the original vessel's propeller was much too small, but with a tripling in diameter the model's propeller efficiency is much better. The scale of this boat is also extremely large, so the "model factor" is less severe than normal. The net result is an actual increase in the admiralty constant.

For the model submarine's shaft power I have

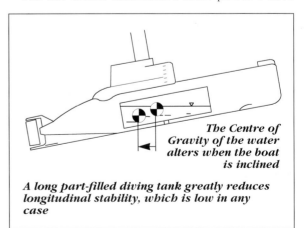

The Centre of Gravity of the water alters when the boat is inclined

A long part-filled diving tank greatly reduces longitudinal stability, which is low in any case

TABLE 2.1: A SELECTION OF SCALE SPEEDS

Name	Scale	$V_{original}$	V_{model}
VII c	1:40	17.0 kn	5.0 km/h
		7.6 kn	2.2 km/h
XXI	1:30	15.6 kn	5.3 km/h
		17.2 kn	5.8 km/h
Seehund	1:10	5.5 kn	3.2 km/h
		6.9 kn	4.0 km/h
Wa202	1:40	24.0 kn	7.0 km/h
V80	1:30	28 kn	9.5 km/h
Schwertwal	1:10	25 kn	14.6 km/h
Class 206	1:40	17 kn	5.0 km/h
TR 1700	1:50	25 kn	6.5 km/h

TABLE 2.2: A SELECTION OF MEASURED ADMIRALTY CONSTANTS

Type	Scale	Displacement	Shaft Power	Speeds	c_b
Class 206	1:1	500 t	1500 PS	17 kn	269
	1:50	5 kg	18 W	8.5 km/h	157
V 80	1:1	76 t	2000 Ps	28 kn	169
	1:30	3.8 kg	25 W	8.7 km/h	100
Type XXI	1:1	1819 t	5000 PS	17.2 kn	80
	1:30	65 kg	375 W	7.5 km/h	28
Type VIIc41	1:1	860 t	750 PS	7.6 kn	68
Forelle	1:1	15.5 t	65 PS	7.75 kn	60
	1:13	5 kg	24 W	7 km/h	65
Delphin	Living	100 kg	2 PS	12.5 m/s	2000

assumed an approximate efficiency of 50%, taking into account relatively poor efficiency and losses due to the speed controller and shaft friction. It would be worthwhile to gather more precise data, but many a good model motor is not documented well enough to allow this. Actual power at the propeller can only be established by measuring the flow with the boat running, and doing this accurately presents considerable problems.

The memory circuit shown below is a means of measuring and recording the value while the submarine is travelling through the water. It can then be read off later on land. In general terms it is important to view all data concerning the model with some care, as there are many possible sources of error which could affect the accuracy of the result.

These include inaccuracies of measurement, especially concerning the vessel's speed. We should also bear in mind that model drive systems, especially the propellers, are not always the exact miniature reproductions which we like to think they are.

The main problem in terms of propellers is the difficulty of matching the screw to the speed of the motor and the vessel. To obtain an accurate match the following formula should be used:

$$V_{Boat} = \frac{1}{1+Slippage} n \times H \times 0.0000167$$

where

V_{Boat}: Boat's speed in m/s
n: Propeller speed in rpm
H: Pitch in mm

Slippage: 0 with spindle stern
20% (= 0.2) with free propeller

This formula only represents a starting point, but even that can be extremely useful.

The roll resulting from propeller torque can become a problem with single-screw boats fitted with powerful motors. The extent of the problem is dictated by the vessel's metacentric height and the torque of the motor. Motor speed is of no account, so it ought to be possible to side-step the problem by installing a high-revving motor of correspondingly low torque.

Unfortunately small propellers are much less efficient than large ones. In fact, for good efficiency the propeller – and thus the torque – needs to be as large as the submarine can take, commensurate with a tolerable heel angle.

The angle of heel is as follows:

$$\alpha = \arcsin\left(\frac{M_d}{m \times g \times MZH}\right)$$

or in other terms:

$$M_d = m \times g \times MZH \times \sin\alpha$$

M_d: Motor torque in Nm
m: Mass of boat in kg
g: Acceleration due to gravity 9.81m/s²
MZH: Metacentric height in m
α: Heel angle in degrees

Example: If we consider a boat weighing 5kg, with a metacentric height of 10mm and an acceptable angle of heel of 5 degrees,

$$5kg \times 9.81m/s^2 \times 0.01m \times \sin(5 Grad) = 0.0427 Nm$$

the maximum motor torque which it can tolerate is:
= 0.0427 Nm. At a rotational speed of 5,000 rpm this gives a shaft power of

$$P = n[Upm]M_d \pi/30$$

$$= 5000 Upm \times 0.0427 Nm \times \frac{3.1415}{30}$$

$$= 22.4 W$$

which equates to an electrical power of about 40 W. With a model of this size that is enough for a speed of 6 to 9km/hr.

An angle of heel of 5 degrees hardly has any effect on the model's control characteristics, and can therefore be considered as acceptable. If the model is trimmed statically with a slight lean in the opposite direction, the "torque roll" will be reduced further. Regulatory systems governing lateral attitude can be fitted to stabilise the model, as can independently moving hydroplanes [the equivalent of ailerons] but this is only necessary with extremely powerful motors.

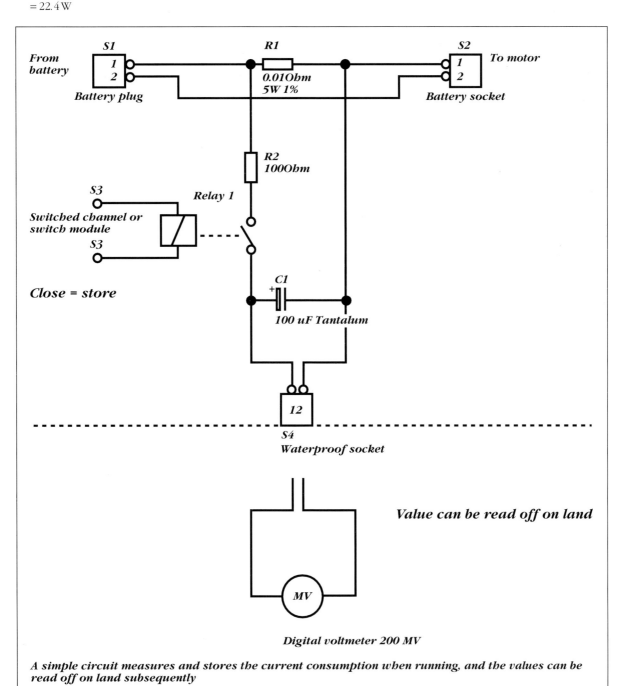

A simple circuit measures and stores the current consumption when running, and the values can be read off on land subsequently

Chapter 3

Hull Construction

Pressure hull strength

The strength required for a surface-running model boat is determined primarily by the forces imposed on it during transport and when the owner or curious onlooker picks it up. This is not the case with the model submarine, where the hull is subject to one crucial load above all others: water pressure. In contrast, all the other forces acting upon it are vanishingly small and can be ignored completely. At a depth of 10m water pressure is 1 bar, which means that a load of about 1kg is exerted on each square centimetre of the hull surface. This is the formula for calculating water pressure:

$$p = ro \times g \times h$$

where

p:	Pressure in bar
ro:	Density of water in kg/m³
	0.998 (fresh water at 20 degrees C)
	1.04 (North Sea water)
g:	Acceleration due to gravity 9.81m/s²
h:	Depth of water in m

What level of stress resistance do we have to design into the pressure hull if it is to be able to cope with all the situations which might arise under water?

The normal operating depth of a model submarine is about 1m (corresponding to 0.1 bar). In large lakes with clear water the operator may even take his boat down to 2 or 3m. We can therefore assume that the maximum submerged depth will be in the order of 4m, corresponding to the high diving area of a swimming pool or a serious error on the part of the operator. If we apply a safety factor of 2 – which should be sufficient for an unmanned system – we obtain a destruction depth of 8m (corresponding to 0.8 bar).

This really represents the acceptable minimum in terms of pressure hull strength if we are aiming at a model submarine which will be safe in all situations. However, there are many model submarines, some of them kit models, which are only built to survive a depth of 2m without damage, but even then their owners are occasionally seen going home without their boat. These models are often equipped with a safety system which enforces a maximum diving depth limit of 2m, at which point the large diving cells are automatically emptied, but even that does not always help. If the boat is running at full forward speed with the hydroplanes set "hard down", the boat dives so quickly that it will easily reach a depth of 4m before the diving cells produce enough buoyancy to raise the model, and by then it is usually too late. Of the models which stay down at the bottom for "unexplained reasons" most are subsequently recovered, but the costs in terms of a salvage diver and subsequent repairs to the model are unlikely to please the owner.

If you want your model submarine to survive, it is vital not to under-estimate the loads acting upon it. An example should make this clear: the pressure on the hull

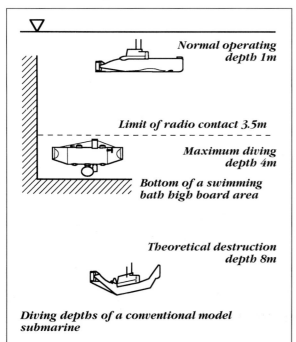

Diving depths of a conventional model submarine

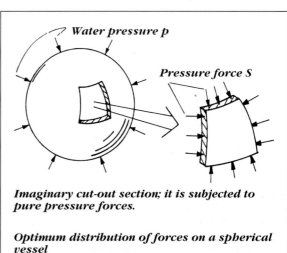

Imaginary cut-out section; it is subjected to pure pressure forces.

Optimum distribution of forces on a spherical vessel

of a small submarine 1m long and 10cm in diameter at an operating depth of one metre is 1 kN, i.e. a weight force of 102kg. When we consider that we are aiming for a destruction depth eight times this figure, the boat should be able to withstand effortlessly a corpulent human sitting bodily on the hull. It is a good idea to keep this in mind when designing and building the hull.

How do we go about building a pressure hull of such strength?

The optimum pressure vessel is a sphere, as the wall material experiences equal pressure loads at every point and in every direction. As a result it is possible to exploit the full strength of the material used for that hull. Research submarines designed to descend to extreme depths are therefore invariably of this shape.

The next best shape is the circular cross-section cylinder, preferably with hemispherical end caps. The cylindrical section also experiences pure pressure loads, but the forces in the lateral (tangential) direction are exactly twice as high as in the longitudinal (axial) direction. Since cylinders are much easier to manufacture from flat steel plate than spheres, this is the standard shape for large submarines.

Both these forms have in common the fact that the hull material is subject to pure pressure loads, i.e. no part of the hull skin has to withstand a bending load. If bending loads were present, much thicker hull walls would be necessary.

All this information applies equally to internally pressurised tanks, although the two types of body fail in fundamentally different ways when overloaded. If the stress S in the wall of an internally pressurised vessel exceeds the limit value Smax specific to the material, the wall ruptures and the vessel explodes like an air balloon.

When a vessel under external pressure fails, the body crumples and distorts as it is compressed, and ends up looking like a squashed drink can. Even then the hull material does not necessarily rupture. In this case the critical load is not determined by the material's maximum stress coefficient Smax, but by its rigidity, defined by the modulus of elasticity E. For the pressure hull of a model submarine it is therefore more important that the material flexes as little

as possible at a given load, than that it fails at a particular load.

To find the critical distortion pressure we use the following formulae, as stated in the specialist literature:

Sphere:

$$P_{kr} = \frac{2 \times E \times h^2}{R^2 \sqrt{3(1-ny^2)}}$$

or turned round:

$$h = \sqrt{\frac{P_{kr} \times R^2 \sqrt{3(1-ny^2)}}{2 \times E}}$$

Cylinder:

$$P_{kr} = \frac{0.25 \times E \times h^3}{R^3(1-ny^2)}$$

or:

$$h = \sqrt[3]{\frac{P_{kr} \times R^3(1-ny^2)}{0.25 \times E}} = 1.54 \sqrt[3]{\frac{P_{kr}}{E}} R$$

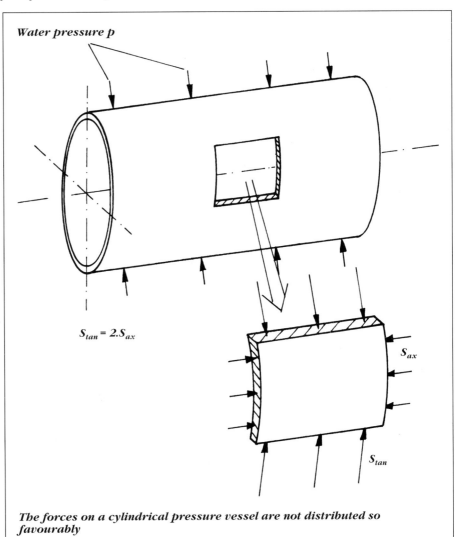

Water pressure p

$S_{tan} = 2.S_{ax}$

S_{ax}

S_{tan}

The forces on a cylindrical pressure vessel are not distributed so favourably

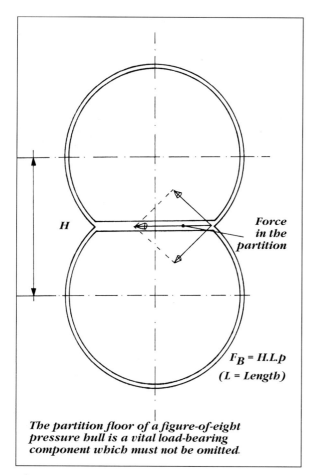

The partition floor of a figure-of-eight pressure hull is a vital load-bearing component which must not be omitted.

H

Force in the partition

$F_B = H.L.p$

$(L = Length)$

where

E:	Modulus of elasticity	in Pa
h:	Wall thickness	in mm
P_{kr}:	Critical pressure	in Pa
R:	Radius	in mm
ny:	Lateral contraction factor 0.3	

Material coefficient E see table 3.1.

$$p \text{ (in bar)} = p\frac{\text{(inPa)}}{10^5}$$

For example, a cylindrical pressure hull of 100mm diameter (R = 50mm) made of fibre laminate (E = 25 . 10{9}Pa, ny = 0.3) a minimum wall thickness of:

$$\sqrt[3]{\frac{8\times10^4 \times Pa(50mm)^3(1-0.3^2)}{0.25\times25\times10^9\times Pa}} = 1.13mm$$

This figure assumes that the vessel is perfectly cylindrical and made of top-quality, low resin content laminate. Any deviation from an exactly cylindrical shape and every fault in the laminate reduces the maximum load significantly. If we cannot be sure of perfection in these aspects, we have to build our models from somewhat thicker material.

The cylinder's end caps deserve special attention. In the ideal case they are of hemispherical form, and since this type of cap will be inherently stronger than the cylindrical hull, they can be made of slightly thinner material than the rest of the pressure hull. At the other extreme we have flat end caps. If this is the only choice, then we have to allow for the caps flexing inward and failing in this way. This danger can only be countered by allowing for a generous wall thickness. If we accept a distortion of 1% of the diameter, then the thickness required is:

$$h = 3.26 \ \sqrt[3]{\frac{P}{E}} \ R$$

This assumes the terms and units as stated above. If we use a wall thickness half of that calculated, the end caps will distort to the extent of 8% of the diameter.

In our example we calculate a wall thickness of 2.4mm, i.e. substantially greater than for the cylindrical section.

TABLE 3.1: MATERIAL COEFFICIENTS OF THE MOST COMMONLY USED MODELLING MATERIALS

Material	Modulus Of Elasticity in GPa 10^9 Pa	Tensile Strength in MPa 10^6 Pa	Density in kg/dm³
Polystyrene PS	3.2	90	1.05
Polymethyl-methacrylate PP	3.0	105	1.18
Polypropylene PP	1.2	43	0.91
Spruce			
longitudinal	16.3	100	0.5
radial	1.1	90	
tangential	0.57		
Balsa			
longitudinal	6.3		
radial	0.3		
tangential	0.11		
Polyester/Chopped strand mat	10	200	1.5
Polyester/Woven glass cloth	25	420	1.88
Steel St37	210	360	7.9
Nirosta (Stainless) 1.4301, V2A	196	500	7.9
Brass Ms63	110	290	8.3

A special form of cylindrical pressure hull is the figure-of-eight design, as used in the electric Type XXI and XXIII submarines. The critical pressure for this hull can be calculated using the same formula, although we also have to allow for a severe compressive load in the centre, and in the model a central strut must be incorporated to absorb this force.

Unfortunately most model submarines do not feature a circular-section pressure hull, and the builder just hopes that it will be strong enough. In my opinion this is not a realistic standpoint. Any deviation from the cylindrical form – and this includes saddle tanks and similar designs – causes considerable bending forces to occur in the hull walls. A hull material which is able to withstand pure pressure loads will not necessarily survive high bending loads, and the builder must be clear on this point.

To get some idea of the magnitude of these bending forces, we take the hull cross-section (e.g. at the main bulkhead) and superimpose on it a circle of the same area, with the excess evenly distributed all round (see diagram). The circle represents a hypothetical pressure hull free of bending moments. The bending moment is now the pressure force in this hypothetical wall multiplied by the distance to the actual hull wall, i.e. the length of the lever.

If we take as our example the main bulkhead of the Type VIIc U-boat, as shown here, and assume that R_{hyp} = 50mm with the hull wall thickness as calculated earlier, then the stress in the hull wall at our presumed destruction depth is 224MPa, i.e. significantly higher than the permissible value of 200. In contrast, the pressure force in the hypothetical pressure hull amounts to only 3.5MPa, so the critical pressure has already been reached, and the hull collapses. Unfortunately it not possible to provide a simple method of calculating the necessary wall thickness under these circumstances. In fact it makes little sense to do so, since in every case it is better not to build hulls of this type. If you insist on making non-circular pressure hulls you can expect them to fail in a different way in any case:

Even if the wall neither ruptures nor collapses under the pressure, it will suffer significant distortion. The change in shape reduces the volume of the submarine, and its upthrust falls in proportion. The net result is that the boat is no longer able to surface once it reaches a particular depth, and it simply continues to descend at an increasing rate. If you make a mistake with a hydroplane command when running a dynamic diving boat with 2% residual upthrust, at a depth of only 3m the boat's residual buoyancy is reduced to zero. The boat sits on the bottom, and its operator may as well start the salvage procedure.

If the pressure hull is cylindrical or spherical these problems simply do not occur since such hulls are very rigid (until they collapse). The change in radius is:

$$\text{Delta R} = \frac{h \times p}{E}$$

Based on the cylinder as described above, this distortion amounts to a mere 3.6um (= 1/300mm) at destruction depth. This equates to a change in volume which in practice is unmeasurably small. If we consider a pressure hull of non-circular cross-section the situation is very different.

Unfortunately the change in volume in this case can

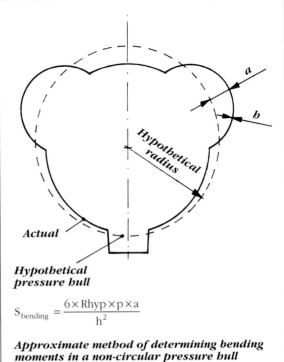

$$S_{bending} = \frac{6 \times R_{hyp} \times p \times a}{h^2}$$

Approximate method of determining bending moments in a non-circular pressure hull

only be calculated using a complex computer program. To get some idea of the magnitude of the distortion we shall consider the flat hatch with which such boats are usually sealed.

Here the following rule applies:

$$s_{max} = \frac{3 \times p \times b^2}{E \times h^2}$$

$$f_{max} = \frac{2.28 \times p \times b^4}{E \times h^3}$$

Delta V = $400 \times a \times b \times f_{max}$

where

S_{max}: Maximum force in Pa
f_{max}: Maximum bending in mm
Delta V: Change in volume in cm³
a,b: Length and width of the plate in mm
h: Thickness of the plate in mm
p: Water pressure in Pa
E: Modulus of elasticity in Pa

A plate made of macrolon (poly-carbonate, E = 2.1 x 10⁹ Pa), 100 x 300 x 5mm in size, is subjected to a maximum force of 91MPz at destruction depth, which it can just withstand (S_{zul} = 100MPa).

According to this formula the amount of flex which occurs is now 65mm, although we have to bear in mind that the formula is only accurate for small distortions. In any case this is clearly too much, since at a depth of only 1m the hatch will distort by 8.1mm. This equates to a loss of volume of 97cm³ at normal operating depth. At the very least this means that it will be impossible to set the boat to stay at a constant depth, and any error on the part of the operator would make it extremely likely that the sub would never be seen again.

Most model submarine accidents which I have personally observed can be laid at the door of inadequate pressure hull rigidity, as outlined above. This is a typical scenario: the boat disappears from view for some reason, but the operator waits a few moments to see if it surfaces again. Who wouldn't? For safety's sake he did not completely fill the diving cell so that there would be a little residual upthrust for just such a situation. Unfortunately the boat has quickly sunk to a depth where the hull is deformed slightly – just enough to reduce the "spare" buoyancy to nothing; the boat thus continues to sink. The operator then decides to empty the diving cells as an emergency surfacing measure, but it is already far too late. The ever increasing distortion has caused leaks, and the boat is now flooded and cannot respond.

It is important not to consider a submarine as a surface ship with the hatches screwed down tight. In full-size subs the pressure hull is always of cylindrical or even spherical form, and for very good reasons. Even though the pressure which water exerts on a model submarine is much lower than in the "full-size" world, the loads are still relatively enormous, and they are now acting on a vessel made not of steel but plastic or wood, both of which are far less rigid. It is therefore sensible in every respect to adopt the same construction for the model as for the full-size vessel; not only in terms of scale fidelity but also for technical reasons. This means that a double-skinned boat, in which the pressure hull and the outer vessel are separate assemblies with different functions, should be modelled as such. In fact this approach does not necessarily involve more work, since pre-fabricated plastic tubing can be used for the pressure hull, and the outer vessel can be of simpler construction.

Constructional methods

Models of conventional surface boats are built using a wide variety of basic methods. First we should consider the classic principles of wood construction using the plank-on-frame, layered (bread-and-butter) construction and moulded wooden hulls consisting of glued planking. A further traditional method is to use steel or brass plate which can be soldered or welded into any shape by skilled hands. These old methods have more recently been complemented by plastics, especially polyester and epoxy resins with glass fibre reinforcement, but also including thermo-plastics, which are the preferred materials for heat moulding in large production runs. These materials can also be glued effectively.

For model submarines ready-made tubing made of polystyrene, plexiglas [perspex], polypropylene and metal can be considered. These are standard industrial semi-finished materials which are relatively cheap to buy, offer excellent dimensional accuracy and also very good strength for use in pressure hulls.

Of these materials the easiest to obtain is polypropylene waste pipe. A 70mm diameter pipe with a wall thickness of 2mm will withstand an external pressure of 0.6 bar, using the methods of calculation outlined already, and this is not quite enough for the required destruction depth. It is also true that these pipes are of extremely imprecise manufacture, and although they are adequate for their designed purpose this imprecision means a distinct reduction in pressure strength for us, so the larger diameters at least are completely unsuitable.

A much better bet are pipes made of poly-methyl-metacrylate (abbreviated to PMMA) – better known under the brand names of Plexiglas and Perspex. They are far more expensive but are harder and much more accurately made. The range of sizes is impressive, as are the quality and workability of the material, and these qualities certainly justify the relatively high price. This pipe can be obtained via any perspex supplier. The material also offers the interesting possibility of making a transparent pressure hull, which allows you to see all the technology at work.

Polystyrene tubing is also manufactured for the use of professional model makers. This material is also extremely accurately made and cheaper, but unfortunately more difficult to obtain.

In contrast, metal pipe of many types is readily available, and the most desirable of them all is stainless steel which makes excellent pressure hulls. Since the necessary wall thickness is not great, these pipes are also of comparable weight to plastic types. Unfortunately metals have a drawback: they are very efficient radio wave shields, which means that the radio control system installation is problematic. At the very least an external aerial is necessary. Unfortunately the pressure hull consists of more than the cylindrical section alone; it also requires two end caps. As already mentioned,

Simple single-skin experimental boat

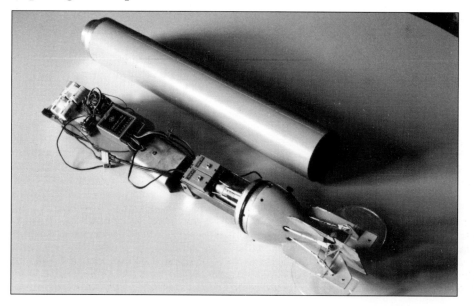

TABLE 3.2: PRESSURE STRENGTH OF VARIOUS TUBES

Material Abbrev.	Diameter x Thickness mm x mm	Permissible Pressure bar	Weight/ Length kg/m	Hatch Thickness mm	
Waste pipe					
PP	50 x 2,.0	1.69	0.39	4.22	
PP	70 x 2.0	0.62	0.56	4.22	
PP	100 x 2.0	0.21	0.80	4.22	Too little
Plexiglas, cast					
PMMA	100 x 5.0	8.24	2.54	10.55	
PMMA	150 x 5.0	2.44	3.87	10.55	
PMMA	200 x 5.0	1.03	5.21	10.55	
PMMA	250 x 5.0	0.53	6.54	10.55	Too little
PMMA	250 x 10.0	4.22	12.82	21.10	
PMMA	300 x 10.0	2.44	15.49	21.10	
Polystyrene, for static modelling					
PS	76 x 3.2	5.21	1.10	6.75	
PS	101 x 3.2	2.24	1.47	6.75	
PS	104 x 3.2	2.05	1.52	6.75	
PS	127 x 3.2	1.13	1.87	6.75	
PS	140 x 3.2	0.84	2.06	6.75	
PS	152 x 3.2	0.66	2.24	6.75	Too little
Stainless Steel					
V2A	50 x 1.0	34.46	1.22	2.11	
V2A	70 x 1.0	12.56	1.71	2.11	
V2A	100 x 1.0	4.31	2.46	2.11	
V2A	150 x 1.0	1.28	3.70	2.11	
V2A	200 x 1.0	0.54	4.94	2.11	Too little
V2A	200 x 1.5	1.82	7.39	3.16	
Gas pipe (very thick, very heavy)					
St37	114 x 4.5	281.65	12.26	9.49	
St37	150 x 4.8	151.24	17.30	10.13	
St37	165 x 4.8	117.21	19.28	10.23	
Brass					
Ms63	100 x 1.0	2.29	2.58	2.11	
Ms63	100 x 2.0	18.29	5.11	4.22	
Ms63	200 x 2.0	2.29	10.33	4.22	
Layer construction or plank on frame					
Kiefer	100 x 8.0	6.41	1.73	16.88	
Kiefer	150 x 12.0	6.41	3.90	25.32	
Kiefer	200 x 16.0	6.41	6.94	33.76	
Balsa	100 x 15.0	8.16	1.00	31.65	
Balsa	100 x 12.0	4.18	0.83	25.32	

the optimum shape of the end caps is hemi-spherical, and if this is possible using the same material, a thinner wall can be used than for the cylinder. Unfortunately hemispheres are only available in polystyrene and metal, but if you are using these materials the ready-made end caps can also be recommended.

With the other materials there is usually no option but to use flat end caps. These offer much lower pressure strength, and a considerably greater wall thickness is required. It is also true that most of the openings in the pressure hull are located in the end caps, and any opening weakens the part further. As a result it is important to be generous when selecting the wall thickness,

and never use a wall thinner than the calculated value. The connection between end cap and cylindrical pipe can be a simple glued joint provided that there is sufficient overlap. In fact the cap does not even need to be attached provided that the seal is watertight, as water pressure will hold it in place reliably.

A pressure hull made in this way can simply be run in its bare state for experimental purposes, i.e. without any external fittings. In fact I strongly recommend that you produce a simple sub of this type initially so that you can gather some initial experience in submarine operation. This will give you a huge start when you decide to build a complex scale boat, as you will understand the problems and solutions so much better. The easiest method of producing a scale model submarine is to convert a cylindrical pressure hull (either the existing one or a new one) by building an external hull over it using any constructional method you like, as it does not have to provide any particular form of strength. This solution gives the modeller a much wider choice of materials and working methods than would be possible if the external vessel were to double up as the pressure hull.

If you decide to model a full-size boat of single-skin construction, naturally the pressure hull has to serve as the outer hull as well. In this case it should be of the same streamlined shape as the original, and be capable of accepting a painted finish and a wealth of detail fittings. A good idea here is to form the bow and stern sections as free flooding voids, with the actual pressure hull sealed by flat end caps. It is usually possible to attach detail fittings to the pipe at a later stage.

If this form of construction is not possible, perhaps because the free flooding voids make it impossible to build in sufficient buoyancy in the case of a small boat, there is only one option open to you: a GRP hull made in a negative mould. This is one of the most complex procedures available to the submarine modeller, but at the same time it is also the most capable and versatile method. In this book I will only touch briefly on the processes involved. If you decide on GRP moulding you

This submarine, of steel plate construction, was made by a Belgian modeller. It is true-scale right down to the rust

will need to study the appropriate specialist literature to gain the detailed information you require.

The starting point is an original model, as accurate and as highly detailed as possible, but made by any method you like. A proven and popular method is bread-and-butter construction using PUR foam with a coating of polyester filler and a careful painted finish based on filler-primer. Welded joints can be shown as strips of narrow adhesive tape. The original model (the "plug") is then treated with mould-release wax before a multi-part negative mould is made directly over it. The negative mould is then used to lay up the actual hull for your model. The moulding will reproduce exactly the same surface structure as the plug and will also be very strong.

If the full-size sub features saddle tanks or a deck superstructure which disturb the circular shape of the pressure hull, it is best to build these parts separately and attach them to the completed pressure hull. This method has no effect on the inherent strength of the pressure hull. If you need the buoyancy of these parts you can fill them with foam. In this case it is essential to consider the pressure strength of the foam, and to apply some form of waterproof sealant to all open surfaces to prevent the material absorbing water.

Hulls can be built from sheet metal, but this procedure is very demanding of the modeller's manual skills. Brass is the usual choice because of its good corrosion resistance, but boats have also been made successfully in mild steel sheet. In this case it is possible to emulate the individual plates and bulkheads of the full-size vessel more accurately than with any other method of construction. Soft soldering, silver soldering and welding are all options for joining the pieces. The result is a hull of considerable rigidity and therefore good pressure strength. Unfortunately the same problems arise in respect of the radio control installation as with metal pipe construction.

Adequately rigid pressure hulls can also be made using timber, provided that you take full account of the directional strength characteristics of the material, i.e. the grain direction. Some of the earliest full-size submarines were made in this way (e.g. Icitineo 2).

Both bread-and-butter and plank-on-frame construction keep the wood grain in the fore-and-aft direction, with the result that the wood fibres are not orientated in the peripheral direction, as is required for maximum compressive strength. However, the stiffness of wood with this grain direction is low (only ⅟₁₅ to ⅟₃₀ of the value for the fore-and-aft orientation), which means that relatively thick walls are required. The grain direction of the bulkheads is much more favourable, and these components therefore bear a large proportion of the load. Unfortunately it is very difficult to produce really accurate joints between planks, as required to transfer the compressive forces evenly to neighbouring strakes. In other words: the manufacturing tolerances are very tight, and it makes sense to include a generous safety factor when calculating the thickness of the pressure hull. Doubling the wall thickness gives an eight-times improvement in the theoretical destruction depth, and this seems appropriate. The glue moulding process results in at some some of the wood fibres running in the peripheral direction, and in this case the necessary strength can be achieved with moderate wall thicknesses.

Chapter 4

Access and Sealing

The top hatch

Here is a model submarine with a free flooding deck with turret, armament and other scale details. Its builder removes the deck to reveal a series of elongated hatches made of transparent plastic, each secured with many screws. The proud owner of this submarine spends the next quarter of an hour removing these screws to gain eventual access to the sub's internal equipment. What we have here is a surface ship with its deck openings screwed down and sealed, in the hope of making a working submarine. Alas, this is not the most promising route.

This method of making a submarine has a very poor prospect of withstanding the pressure it will encounter

This popular style of screw-secured hatch is derived from a surface-running model boat, but is inadequate to withstand water pressure

under water. As already explained in the chapter entitled "Hull Construction", flat hatches are very prone to flexing, and water pressure bows them inwards significantly. If you want to keep the bending within reasonable limits – such as 1% of the hatch width – then you can use the following formula to find the necessary thickness:

$$h = 6.1 \sqrt[3]{\frac{p}{E}}\, b$$

Terms and units as used earlier.

For a polycarbonate hatch 10cm wide this turns out to be 20.5mm – a substantial hatch indeed, and quite difficult to produce. Note that halving the material thickness will result in an increase in distortion of eight times!

The large openings also greatly weaken the hull itself. The force of water pressure acting on the hull walls is transmitted to the hatches via the retaining screws – a most inefficient transfer medium – and the bending moments are not transmitted at all. As a result this form of hatch is found primarily in model submarines with non-circular pressure hulls whose constructor is not aware of the likely loads the boat will encounter.

Maintaining the boat is very difficult since the only

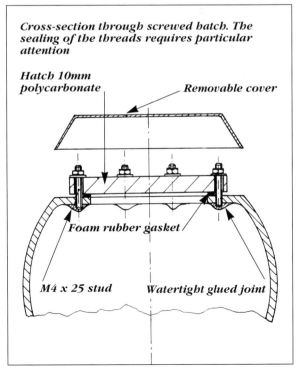

Cross-section through screwed hatch. The sealing of the threads requires particular attention

Hatch 10mm polycarbonate

Removable cover

Foam rubber gasket

M4 x 25 stud   **Watertight glued joint**

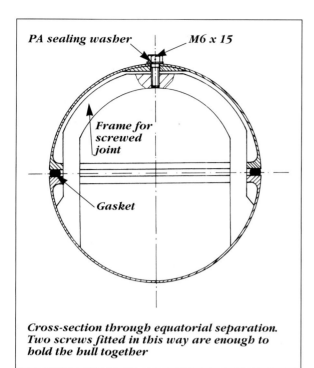

Cross-section through equatorial separation. Two screws fitted in this way are enough to hold the hull together

access to the internal equipment is through the extremely narrow openings, and if you have big hands you are in real trouble. Not to mention the time-consuming task of doing up and undoing all those screws.

Basically I want to dissuade modellers from using this type of construction, but if there is no other option you should be aware of the solutions to the most common problems. The seal usually consists of foam rubber of round cross-section, stuck down to the hull using contact cement. An alternative method is to grease the hatch thoroughly with hand cream and then glue the hatch to the hull using one-shot silicone sealant. Once the silicone has vulcanised right through, the hatch can be removed to leave a perfectly fitting gasket. The screwed

joint should consist of a length of brass studding fixed permanently to the hull every two or three centimetres. The hatch is then held in place with nuts. If you take the opposite route there is a danger of water running through the threads and getting inside the hull cavity in that way.

Equatorial separation

The equator of a sub hull is the line of greatest width, i.e. the centreline if the cross-section is circular. If the hull is divided at that point only a few screws are needed to keep it watertight. This is because the two half-shells are rigid – in contrast to flat plates – and therefore distribute the screw force evenly over the whole area of the seal. The gasket can again be foam rubber or silicone rubber, but O-ring cord and window sealing tape are other possibilities.

An equatorial separation line divides the pressure hull at a point of average load. Only pressure forces arise at the joint line, i.e. there are no additional bending moments. Admittedly the soft seal itself, which is not located exactly flush with the hull wall, disturbs the circular shape of the pressure hull significantly, and therefore the wall thickness at that point must be greater to preserve the overall compressive strength of the hull. Access to the internal fittings is extremely good since the top shell can be folded up and out of the way.

Sealing ring

On the other hand, if we divide the hull vertically and transversely, we find further advantages: the pressure hull is cut through in the plane of minimum load (axial stress = ½ tangential stress), the gasket is as small as it can be, and its outline is a simple circle, which means that it can be machine-made. As a result it is easy to produce a very accurate sealing arrangement which can be kept small and neat.

In this arrangement the internal fittings are installed on a bearer frame which can be withdrawn after the shell has been opened, thus giving optimum accessibility from all sides. Those components which pass through hull openings – the drive motor, rudder and hydroplane servos and so on – are best mounted permanently on the hull, otherwise releasable couplings are necessary.

A boat of this configuration can be held together by a single screw at the bow which engages in the bearer frame and thus connects to the stern section. Another possibility is to fit a small number of screws around the periphery of the sealing ring. The screws are

Equatorial separation gives good access to internal fittings

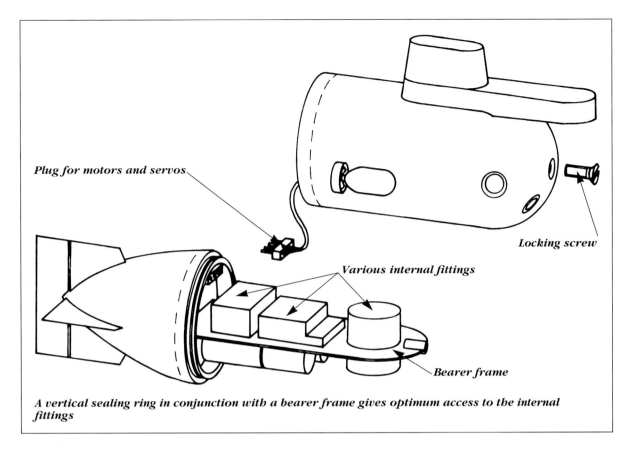

Plug for motors and servos

Various internal fittings

Locking screw

Bearer frame

A vertical sealing ring in conjunction with a bearer frame gives optimum access to the internal fittings

only required to hold the sections together for surface running; when submerged water pressure forces the two sections firmly together. If you are very confident that the vessel is completely watertight, all you need to do is suck a little air out of the internal cavity, and the low pressure inside will hold the sections together.

A similar arrangement is used in some full-size submarines: the hulls of the small "Seehund" and "Forelle" vessels can be separated by undoing one or more screwed pairs of bulkheads in order to gain access to internal equipment.

An interesting idea might be to arrange two separation joints: one at the maximum diameter and one immediately forward of the drive motor. This should be an effective solution for a model since the motor and control surface servos are installed in the stern section, and would be easily accessible once the rear separation point was opened. However, the main equipment frame would not fit through the small opening, so a second separation line and annular seal are needed at the widest point of the hull. The bow hydroplane servos can be installed in the front hull section, and the relatively large opening and short bow hull section allow good access to these parts for servicing.

With this arrangement the obvious choice for gaskets is O-rings, as they provide seals of small cross-section and are also extremely reliable. The O-rings can either be compressed axially between two plates or radially between two pipe sections. With the first method the necessary pressure is applied by the retaining screw located in the bow. Loosen the screw, and the joint separates automatically. If, on the other hand, the O-ring is located between two pipe sections, then this screw is not necessary. The compression of the seal is achieved by making the gap about 10% smaller than the O-ring, so that it is compressed when the sections are pushed together. Friction at the seal will hold the hull components together, and they just need to be held in position by a few screws around the periphery. Lubricating the O-ring with stiff grease will keep the friction within manageable limits.

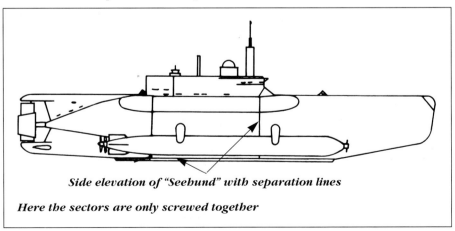

Side elevation of "Seehund" with separation lines

Here the sectors are only screwed together

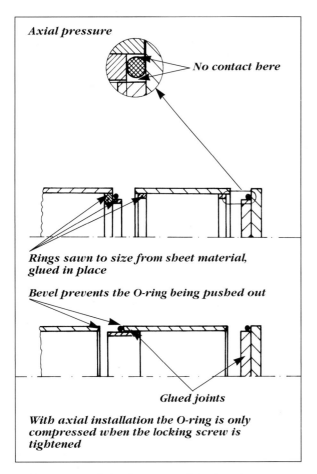

Axial pressure

No contact here

Rings sawn to size from sheet material, glued in place

Bevel prevents the O-ring being pushed out

Glued joints

With axial installation the O-ring is only compressed when the locking screw is tightened

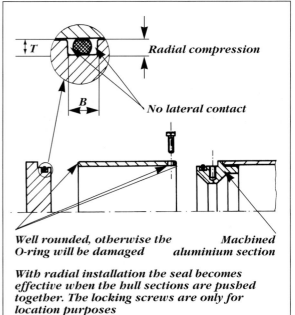

Radial compression

T

B

No lateral contact

Well rounded, otherwise the O-ring will be damaged

Machined aluminium section

With radial installation the seal becomes effective when the hull sections are pushed together. The locking screws are only for location purposes

a perfectly flat, smooth surface, so as far as possible you should arrange for these surfaces to be non-worked sheet material.

A further refinement of the design would be to integrate the retaining system or latch into the sealing ring in the form of a bayonet mount. This would mean that no retaining screws would be needed, and the frame would not be subject to the retaining load. The drawing shows a bayonet system which can be made if you have access to a lathe and a milling machine with dividing head. An alternative latching system could be made using screw-in pins and hand-filed channels. The frame should be designed in such a way that a rotation of the hull sections through about 15° suffices to open and close the hull.

Access to a lathe is very useful when it comes to making the sealing ring. With a lathe you can produce precision-made parts which in turn let you use a small gasket. However, a lathe is not absolutely essential, and you can make serviceable parts with the careful use of a fretsaw. It is important that the O-ring should engage on

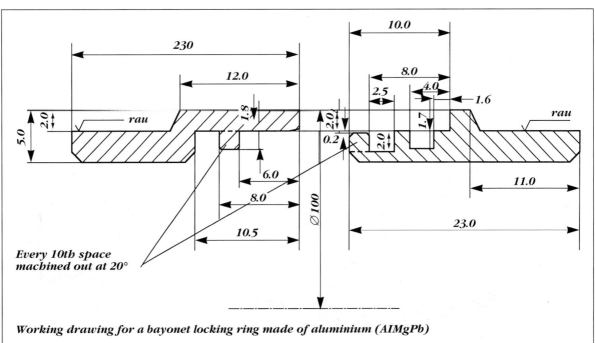

Every 10th space machined out at 20°

Working drawing for a bayonet locking ring made of aluminium (AlMgPb)

Chapter 5

Hull Openings

To the inexperienced submarine modeller in particular the numerous linkages and shafts which have to pass through the pressure hull wall are the cause for anxiety and even sleepless nights. These are problem areas for the surface boat too, but they are usually neglected – after all, a real ship always has a little water in the bilges. Not so with model submarines, where effective seals are a fundamental requirement. On the one hand the pressure which tends to push water through any gaps is much higher, and on the other a model submarine alters its depth with the slightest change in weight, because the residual buoyancy available is much less than with most surface vessels.

Fortunately shaft sealing is a common technical problem, with the result that many ready-made industrial solutions are available. Some of them are even manufactured in the sizes and pressure ranges which we need.

Shaft sealing

It is tempting to think that the usual method based on a grease-filled stern tube and propeller shaft, as used in ordinary model boats, will be suitable for a model submarine. The internal diameter of the tube is at least 1mm larger than the shaft, and is fitted with a close-fitting sleeve bearing at each end. A grease nipple is fitted so that the space between the bushes can be filled with a stiff, water-resistant grease which blocks the water's route into the hull cavity. It is indeed possible to seal submarine propeller shafts in the same way, but although they are extremely easy to install they do not form a reliable seal, especially at high pressures. The bearings must be kept in excellent condition and the grease must be replaced regularly, otherwise you can expect a considerable amount of water to penetrate. This system makes high demands on the grease: primarily that it does not emulsify when in contact with water.

In fact the standard solution to the problem of drive shaft seals is the shaft sealing ring, also known under the trade name "Simmerring". These are rubber elements about the size of a ballrace. They feature a narrow sealing lip, pressed onto the shaft by a small coil spring. The

A variety of standard commercial seals

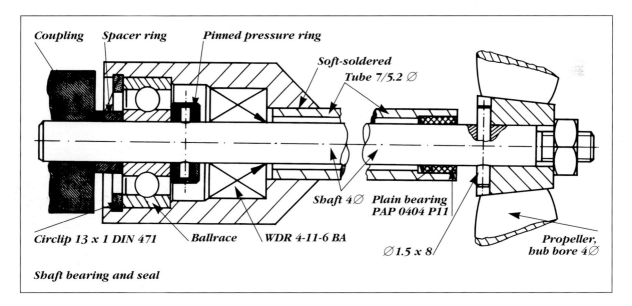

Coupling | **Spacer ring** | **Pinned pressure ring**

Soft-soldered Tube 7/5.2 ⌀

Shaft 4⌀ | **Plain bearing PAP 0404 P11**

Circlip 13 x 1 DIN 471 | **Ballrace** | **WDR 4-11-6 BA**

⌀1.5 x 8

Propeller, hub bore 4⌀

Shaft bearing and seal

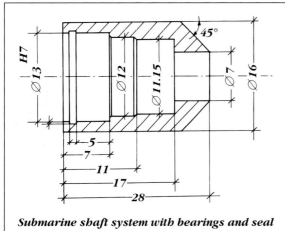

Submarine shaft system with bearings and seal

spring pressure is just high enough to form an effective seal without causing unnecessarily high levels of friction.

Standard sizes start with seals designed for 4mm diameter shafts, with an outside diameter of 11mm. Compact versions with reduced outside dimensions are available, and these are fitted with lip rings similar to those available for needle roller bearings, but their sealing efficiency is not so good. Here again the smallest size fits a 4mm shaft. For smaller shafts O-rings have proved a good solution even though they were never intended for this application.

In general terms you have to bear in mind that friction losses in the drive shaft rise steeply as you increase the shaft diameter, and most of the friction is caused by the seal. Therefore you should select the smallest possible shaft that will perform its function. Note also the significance of rotational speed: the higher the revs, the greater the friction losses.

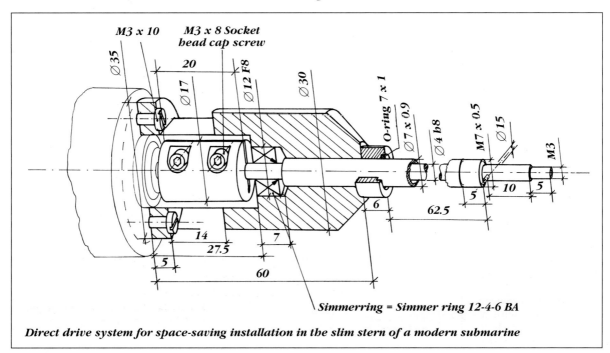

Simmerring = Simmer ring 12-4-6 BA

Direct drive system for space-saving installation in the slim stern of a modern submarine

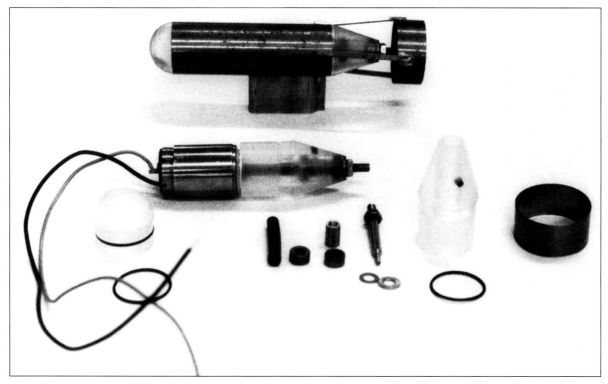

Component parts of the "Penguin B3" motor pod

It is best to locate the sealing element at the front shaft bearing, where its size is of little account. The stern tube can then be filled with grease in the usual way. This avoids the danger of lubricating the seal with water only, which would shorten its useful life dramatically. The rear shaft bearing – immediately forward of the propeller – can take the form of a plain bush. Plain bearings of small diameter can be used, and their small size helps to promote an undisturbed flow of water to the propeller. Materials containing teflon make good bearings, especially DU (German trade name) bronze-backed dry bushes. These are standard commercial bushes which require no lubrication, but which manage well with the slight lubricant quality of water. The design of these bearings makes them able to absorb radial forces only; for example, forces due to propeller imbalance.

For this reason it is necessary to fit a standard ballrace as the front shaft bearing which can also absorb the axial forces due to propeller thrust. To cope with this load the shaft must be axially located in the bearing using two collets. Since the bearing is within the sealing ring it is protected from water and can be lubricated with a little grease (these races are supplied grease-packed). Take care that the sealing ring is not damaged by threads or burrs on the shaft when you install it.

A particular problem in submarines with a spindle [i.e. very slim] stern – and that means virtually all modern, high-speed designs – is the small amount of space available in the slim tip of the hull.

Installing the coupling between the motor and propeller shaft is particularly tricky, since the motor

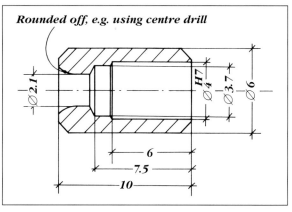

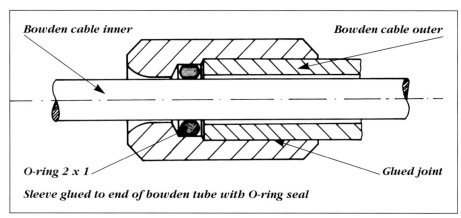

Sleeve glued to end of bowden tube with O-ring seal

obstructs the area completely and you cannot reach the retaining screws. The problem can be circumvented by using an overlength shaft, thereby moving the coupling to an area where access is better, but much valuable space is lost in this way.

A proven solution is to fit a direct-drive system without a flexible coupling, with the motor casing connected to the stern tube by means of a custom-made machined component. The whole assembly is then slid into the stern from the front and retained with a nut located immediately in front of the propeller. A bulkhead is required in the hull to attach the motor and prevent it rotating.

The two shafts [motor and propeller] are connected by means of a block clamp inside the drive assembly. This type of connection ensures true running, unlike a joint using grubscrews. This arrangement eliminates the need for a front bearing altogether, as the propeller thrust is absorbed by the motor bearings (ballraces).

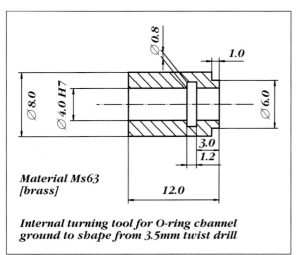

Material Ms63 [brass]

Internal turning tool for O-ring channel ground to shape from 3.5mm twist drill

Many research submarines are powered by external motor pods, and it is extremely difficult to provide effective seals for these features. Unfortunately any water which gets inside is not usually noticed for several weeks, by which time it has wrecked the motor. The photograph shows a successful system with an outside diameter of 25mm and a lip ring shaft seal just in front of the propeller. An important feature is that the pod is ventilated through the cable duct, so that any condensation can evaporate.

Sealing the control surface linkages

A usable emergency solution to this problem is to use a simple shaft and pack it in good grease, but a better, simpler and more permanent answer is to install rubber bellows. Model shops can supply bellows, but car accessory shops should also be investigated, as they supply bellows for handbrake cables in a range of sizes. The bellows are pushed onto the pushrod at one end and a tube glued in the pressure hull tail piece at the other, secured with soft wire or cable ties. The more thorough amongst you will probably apply silicone sealant between them.

For small models however, the change in volume when the control surfaces are moved is too great, and other types of seal have to be used. This also applies if you are building a submarine of single-skin construction, as the bellows are inevitably visible and tend to spoil the scale appearance more than somewhat.

Bowden cables as used in model aircraft can be used, sealed by an O-ring (2 x 1mm) located in a turned holder at the end of the outer sleeve. Unfortunately, although such a gasket is effective, water will usually flow through the space between the plastic bowden inner and the wire core inside it. A little glue applied to this area gets round this problem.

If the pushrod is located entirely inside the pressure hull the shaft of the rudder or hydroplane itself has to be sealed. The skilled machinists amongst you can simply cut an O-ring channel in the bearing sleeve.

However, a drill press and the right size of drill can certainly produce a seating for a slightly thicker O-ring if you don't own a lathe.

Other hull openings

Avoid them wherever possible. Of course, any opening can be sealed using the methods described above, but every gasket represents another weak point which could fail. The fewer you have, the longer your sub will run without problems.

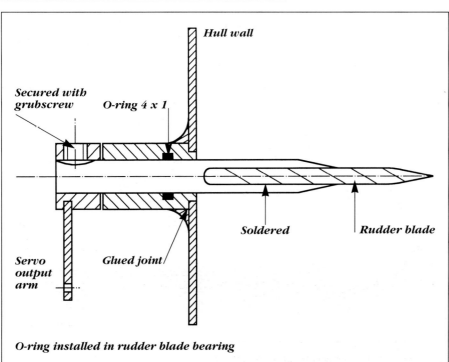

Secured with grubscrew

O-ring 4 x 1

Hull wall

Soldered

Rudder blade

Servo output arm

Glued joint

O-ring installed in rudder blade bearing

For the essential electrical circuits it is possible to use a contact-less switching system. Two reed contacts (small glass tubes with internal contacts which close under the influence of a magnet) can be located close to the outer hull skin. The reed switch operates a bi-stable relay: contact 1 brings the relay to the working position, switching on the receiving system power circuit; contact 2 moves it back to the idle position. To switch the receiving system on and off all you do is stroke a powerful permanent magnet along the appropriate part of the hull, and the system works as if by magic.

If you have electrical circuits in the free flooding voids, perhaps to power auxiliary working systems or lights, then they must be insulated against water over their entire length. Even the tiniest opening will result in powerful corrosion through the galvanic effect of the current. This even occurs in fresh water, with the result that the conductors are simply eaten away to nothing in a few hours.

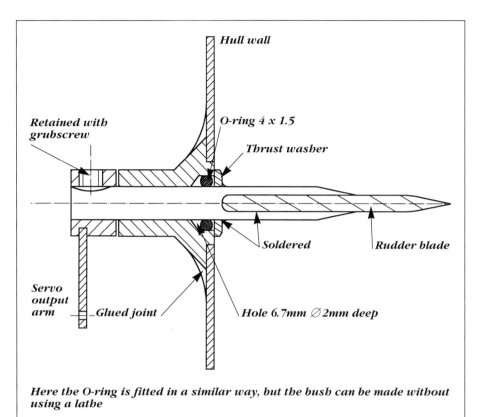

Here the O-ring is fitted in a similar way, but the bush can be made without using a lathe

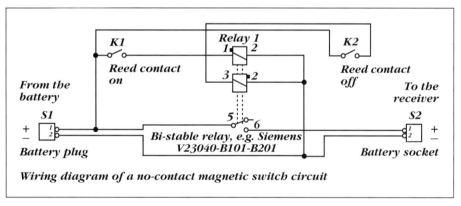

Wiring diagram of a no-contact magnetic switch circuit

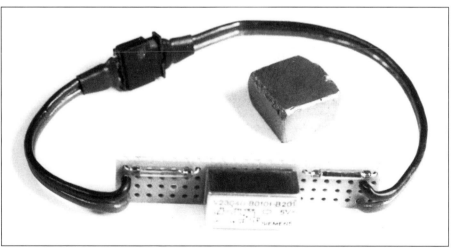

An ultra-compact magnetic switch system

Chapter 6

Diving Tanks

The purpose of the diving tanks is two-fold: on the one hand, to adjust the submarine's weight to to the exact value required to keep the vessel at a constant depth when submerged, and on the other, to provide the necessary upthrust for surfacing and surface running when emptied. To achieve accurate control over the boat's "hovering" ability we need fine control of the quantity of ballast water in the tank. From that state the boat can then carry out static rise-and-fall movements under weight control.

Even in full-size submarines many widely varying systems are used to alter the boat's weight, depending on the type of vessel and the year of its construction. All the variants can be adapted for model use, as well as other systems which for reasons of strength are not suitable for use in full-size boats.

In military subs the speed at which the vessel can submerge is crucial; i.e. the time which elapses between the opening of the flood valves and the disappearance of the conning tower. As with other considerations of time and scale, the scale conversion of this diving speed is bound up with much confusion and many erroneous ideas. In any case a 1:1 conversion is never right.

Let us start by considering the ship's clock fitted to our model submarine. Its progress is controlled by a pendulum, the classic mechanical measure of time. The duration of its swing is:

$$T = 2\pi \sqrt{\frac{\text{Pendulum length}}{\text{Acceleration due to gravity}}}$$

i.e. it is proportional to the square root of the pendulum length.

If we reduce this length by, say, one hundred times, i.e. we build a miniature version of it, the cycle time is reduced to one tenth. Thus time runs faster by the square root of the scale!

Using the same analogy, imagine a 1:40 scale model of a full-size submarine which can submerge in 40 seconds. The time for the model is now:

$$\frac{40s}{\sqrt{40}} = 6.3s.$$

Aspirated, pumped tank

If surface ships are your starting point, this is the most obvious solution:

The diving tank is a rigid, fixed container which is is fitted with an open vent pipe at the top, similar to a fuel tank. In the bottom there is a valve; when the valve is opened water can flow in from outside. A centrifugal pump or geared pump forces the water out again when you want the boat to surface.

And therein lies the crucial disadvantage of this method: if vent pipe is under water – and that is usually the case when the boat is submerged – nothing happens, because only water flows in through the vent pipe instead of air; the tank just stays full.

A different means must be provided of ensuring that the boat surfaces: in the simplest case just enough ballast is added to leave sufficient residual buoyancy even when the diving tank is completely flooded (no air bubbles – not even in the corners!). In this state only the conning tower projects above the water's surface, and the boat actually dives dynamically, i.e. using the motor and the hydroplanes. With this arrangement the vessel's ability to manoeuvre under water is limited to fairly high speed running, as is the case with boats which can only dive dynamically. At low speeds the boat surfaces automatically.

For other submarines – in particular the vessels of the first and second World Wars, which floated very high when at the surface – a good solution is a combination of an aspirated tank with a small piston tank acting as a

Vent
Diving cell
Diving cell floods
Open
Flood valve
Emptying pump

Vent under water
Pump working
Emptying not possible

Pump working
Diving tank empties

Principle of the pump-emptied tank, showing switched positions. A simple pump-emptied tank cannot be emptied under water

control cell. This control cell only requires a volume of about 1 per cent of the boat's weight, but provides the operator with the means of adjusting the sub's constant depth setting accurately. It also allows the boat to rise and fall statically.

Once at the surface the pump can empty the large diving tank, which in some cases makes make up 30 per cent of the vessel's weight.

This combination system is similar to that used in full-size submarines, which also carry a control cell and separate diving tanks. However, it does lack the facility to empty the diving cells completely. For example, if a major inflow of water should occur, or the boat should get stuck in mud, it may not be possible to force the submarine to surface.

One servo operates the home-made flood valve and the switch for the emptying pump

Large-volume diving tanks can be accommodated in areas of the boat to which access is difficult, such as the saddle tanks, the bow space or the stern cavity. The control cell is relatively small and space can easily be found at the sub's centre of gravity.

The flood valve must have a large cross-section, as the pressure difference is only that produced by the difference in water level in the diving cell and outside, which is quite small. Ordinary magnetic valves are available commercially for use in pneumatic systems (see "Compressed air") but their nominal openings are only 2 to 5mm in diameter, and flooding the tanks may take several minutes as a result.

A good solution to the valve problem is a home-made seating valve, held closed by a spring. A servo pushes the valve open in the "dive" setting, and operates the pump switch at the "empty" setting. The pump can be a centrifugal type as it is not required to work against high pressure, but it should be capable of pumping large volumes. Naturally other types of pump can also be used.

If you are using a pump without a non-return valve, it is important to arrange the outflow pipe well above the waterline when the boat is static, otherwise the diving tank will slowly fill up when the boat is on the surface.

Flexible tanks

This type of tank can also be emptied when under water. The principle is even simpler than the aspirated tank:

The flexible diving tank can be a rubber bag or a soft plastic bottle into which water is forced by a pump. As it

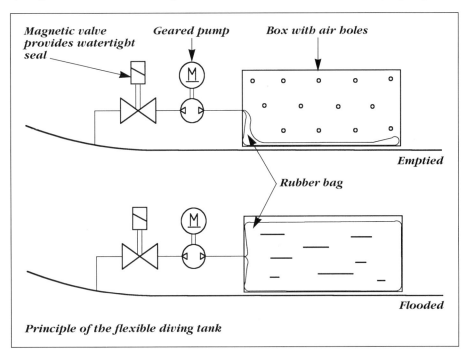

Principle of the flexible diving tank

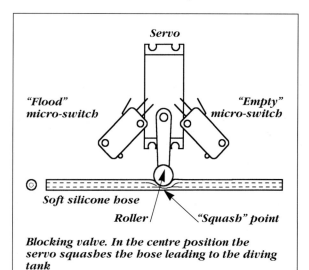

Blocking valve. In the centre position the servo squashes the hose leading to the diving tank

is blown up it compresses the air inside the boat slightly. To empty the bag the pump is reversed, the diving tank contracts, and the air in the boat expands again.

In practice the rubber bag should be installed in its own, ventilated chamber so that it does not chafe on other internal fittings. The chamber also restricts its volume when flooded. This is essential in order to have proper control over the boat's weight when it is submerged. Controlling the quantity of water in the bag is difficult when you have no built-in limits. Do I need to explain what would happen if a fault arose and the pump stayed set permanently to "flood"? Water would be pumped steadily into the bag until it burst!

This system requires a pump which can work in both directions and continue to work against full water pressure when the boat is submerged. Suitable types include geared pumps (car windscreen washer pumps), vane cell pumps, and piston pumps (radial and axial).

Unfortunately most of these pumps are not quite watertight when at rest, with the result that the contents of the diving tank change slowly according to water pressure and the internal pressure of the boat. This can be crucial, since a few grammes in either direction are sufficient to prevent the submarine staying at a constant depth, so it is necessary to eliminate the problem by installing a blocking valve.

A pneumatic magnetic valve (without servo assistance) can be used for this purpose, because the pump

produces sufficient pressure to flood and empty the tanks quickly even when the additional resistance of the small valve opening is taken into account. The cheaper solution is a home-made servo-operated valve.

For the flexible tank itself there are many possible candidates. A length of bicycle or car inner tube contained in a rigid pipe and fitted with two end caps has proved effective. Another useful idea is the flexible tube of plastic used in food etc. These are so strong when filled that an outer sleeve is simply not necessary. Flexible tanks can also be stowed in spaces which are complex in shape and therefore difficult to exploit, although only inside the pressure hull, of course.

A variant of this system uses a rigid tank instead of a flexible one, but with a hole at its highest point venting to the internal boat cavity.

To ensure that the switch cuts off at the right time when the tank is flooded, a water sensor can be installed a few centimetres below the vent opening. Alternatively a float valve could be used to seal the opening. If a hose is connected between the vent hole and the bilges, any bilge water would be sucked out at the same time when the diving cell is emptied.

This appears to be such an ingenious option that it is disappointing to find that it has an inherent drawback: it maintains a high level of humidity inside the boat at all times, and this does not benefit either the reliability of the electronics or the long-term condition of the metal parts. This occurs because the air inside the diving tank is bound to be very damp, and the humid air is sucked into the boat every time the tank is flooded.

A further potential problem is that we can only be sure that water will not enter the boat via the vent opening if the boat remains horizontal. If the boat rolls substantially – as tends to happen during diving manoeuvres – it is possible for the water level in the diving cell to reach the vent opening before it reaches the water sensor.

When we are considering a hermetically sealed submarine, it is better in every case to prevent bilge water collecting than to install a system for pumping it out again later.

Piston tanks

Submarine designs dating from the 17th Century show a diving tank in the form of a cylinder with a piston actuated by a rack and pinion device. Wilhelm Bauer's successful "Seeteufel", built in 1855, was also controlled by such a system. Tanks of this type are the most complex solution to the problem, but they are also the most accurate and therefore the best for our purpose.

The precision is due to the fact that the quantity of water moved by the piston is completely predictable, and its strokes when filling and emptying the tank can also be measured and adjusted accurately.

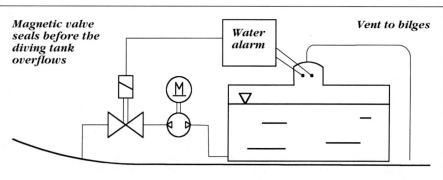

A tank open at the top can be used instead of a flexible tank provided that you ensure that it cannot overflow

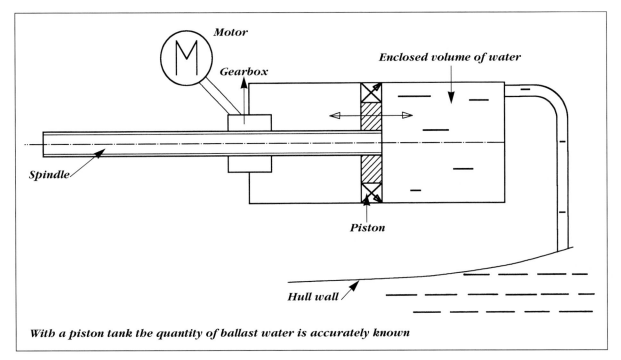

Spindle

Motor

Gearbox

Enclosed volume of water

Piston

Hull wall

With a piston tank the quantity of ballast water is accurately known

Since there is no air bubble in the tank under normal circumstances, the quantity of water moved does not vary with pressure, and the boat's centre of gravity does not alter with changes in attitude. The complications of the piston tank are due to the fact that hardly any ready-made items (such as pumps or valves) can be used, and many of the parts have to be home-made, including some which present mechanical problems. However, one ready-made piston tank is made by the German company of Aeronaut, and it is available through specialist model shops.

The simplest parts of the piston tank are the cylinder and piston: if you do not own a lathe you can base your system on large syringes or pneumatic cylinders, or alternatively a rubber bellows system such as those used in car steering gearboxes. These do not require accurately made connecting pieces and are reliably watertight, but they need considerable space since they cannot be compressed completely. Of course, with a lathe you can produce the cylindrical parts quickly and easily.

The pipe used for the cylinder should have as smooth an internal surface as possible; i.e. the only metal pipes which are suitable are seamless types made of brass, copper or stainless steel. These are often too heavy for small boats, so plastic is the preferred material for them. In this case polystyrene and plexiglas are generally the first choice, since pipes with a smooth internal surface are available in these materials. Although Plexiglas produces beautiful diving tanks, it has a crucial drawback: in the course of time the material absorbs up to 2% water, and in so doing swells. Incidentally polyamide materials (nylon) suffer from the same problem, but swell more quickly. Since the cylinder is always wet – even after several months laid up at home – this is a real problem.

Unfortunately standard commercial waste piping is so "wavy" inside that it only makes a viable cylinder if the piston is fitted with a large, very flexible seal. If you have more patience than spare cash you might care to rummage through the stocks of all your local building

materials suppliers, as you will sometimes find waste piping with a smooth internal surface. An excellent solution in every respect is a GRP pipe laminated onto a polished core to produce a fine, scratch-free inside surface, but many modellers are not prepared to make the effort required.

If a metal cylinder is used, then the piston should be made of the same material as the pipe as powerful electro-chemical corrosion occurs between different metals. This cannot happen with plastic components.

Piston seals can be made from any of the vast range of pneumatic gaskets available. Note that most hydraulic gaskets are designed for much higher pressures, and are too stiff for our purposes. O-rings have proved extremely useful, as they only require a shallow channel, which allows us to use a one-piece piston. Many model submariners also use special industrial seals such as "Airzet" rings (made by Merkel: see appendix) which offer particularly low friction. Refer to the manufacturer's catalogues for details of the range of sizes available and the exact dimensions of these seals.

The piston is normally actuated by a threaded spindle with an M6 or M8 thread. Such a system always works, but it is by no means the last word on the subject. Standard threads are designed to perform as simple fixings, and friction levels are deliberately high to ensure that the fixing does not work loose by itself. Used as a spindle drive a standard thread is less than 20% efficient! Trapezoidal threads are slightly better at 20-30% efficiency, and these can be obtained in 10mm diameter and larger sizes. However, the only really good solution is the recirculating ball spindle and the pulley spindle, which offer efficiencies of over 90%. At this point I can hear many modellers lamenting: "what's the point? An ordinary screw thread works fine!" True enough, but the drive motor and its control system have to be five times as powerful as is actually necessary, and are correspondingly large and heavy.

Unfortunately recirculating ball spindles cost at least 150 DM [60 quid], which is really too much for our

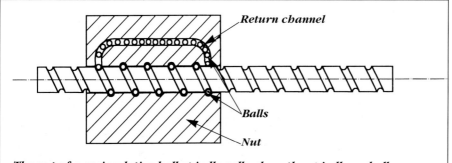

The nut of a recirculating ball spindle rolls along the spindle on balls, producing very little friction. As the balls become free they are passed back to the nut via a return channel

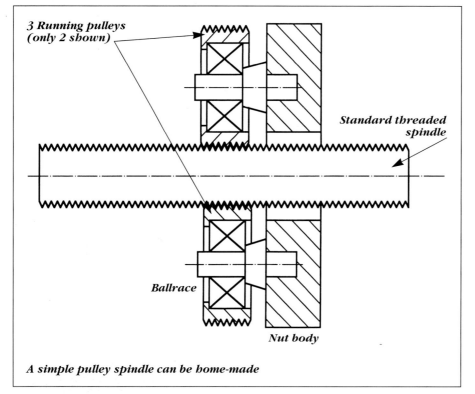

A simple pulley spindle can be home-made

purposes. A form of roller spindle can certainly be made by any good machinist if he has the appropriate tools. Standard rack and pinion devices also work at better than 90% efficiency, although they require a higher reduction ratio in the gearbox than with a spindle drive.

Clearly this arrangement is not self-locking, which means that the piston can move the motor as well as the other way round, because the friction of a normal thread is simply absent. The low-friction types of spindle mentioned above are also non self-locking. However, this only causes problems if you fit a simple control system based on a relay or switches, which does not feed back information on the piston's position. This method of piston control is still widely used, and is the reason why many a model submarine suddenly dives without warning, because the operator does not realise that the piston is being moved by water pressure. If you are not prepared to install an auxiliary motor brake you probably have to accept poor efficiency if you want to achieve an accurate buoyancy control system.

If the diving tank is operated as a servo, as described in a later chapter, the lack of a self-locking actuation system is no disadvantage as the servo electronics register the unwanted piston movement and force the servo motor to compensate for it. In this case the high efficiency level is particularly useful, as it means that a much smaller electronic system is required, with a marked reduction in current drain.

The spindle nut or gear normally runs in a ballrace which is installed at the motor end of the diving tank cover. The final, large gearbox gear is then attached to the spindle nut directly – usually by soldering.

The gearbox can be home-made in its entirety, or alternatively a geared motor with a suitable reduction ratio can be pressed into service. The motor is then connected to the spindle nut by means of an additional pair of gears. If you are using a rack and pinion system the motor can drive the pinion directly.

Any standard D.C. motor designed to be used as a drive motor can be employed to move the piston. The power and reduction ratio required should be calculated beforehand, at least approximately:

$$0.5 I_{max} \times U = P_{elek} = \frac{P_{max} \times 0.0000785 \times D^2 \times L}{T_{stell} \times eta_{getr} \times eta_{mot}}$$

where
I_{max}:   Stall current in A
U: Voltage in V
P_{elek}:   Electrical motor power in W
P_{max}:   Pressure at design diving depth in bar
D: Piston diameter in mm
L: Piston stroke in mm
T_{stell}:   Stroke time in seconds
eta_{getr}:   Efficiency of gearbox + spindle
0.1   For normal thread
0.5   For rack, special spindles
eta_{mot}:   Motor efficiency

(at this power level – not the maximum value)

It is important to select a motor which is working at maximum power output at the boat's nominal diving depth, as shown in the manufacturer's data supplied with it. A useful approximation of this point is half the motor's no-load speed and half its stall current (stalled motor at full voltage). At this setting most motors will be working close to maximum efficiency at the average diving depths which are likely to occur, but they will still have reserves of power if the sub goes lower than the design diving depth. The same applies if the battery is beginning to fail and the operating voltage falling off. The formula can also be used for a flexible tank if you use eta_{pump} instead of eta_{getr}.

Once you have established the best motor speed and voltage, the reduction ratio is found as follows:

$$i = \frac{n_{max} \times h \times T_{stell}}{120 \times L}$$

where

n_{max}: no-load speed in rpm
h: pitch of spindle in mm
i: reduction ratio

In order to calculate power we need to include piston force in the calculation:

$$F = p_{max} \times 0.0785 \times D^2$$

where F = piston force in N

It is really essential that you make this calculation in the first instance, otherwise you will have no idea of the loads occurring in the system, and it will also give you a guideline when you come to estimate the requirements for a new model at some time. For an accurate calculation please refer to the specialist literature.

The only other potential problem which ought to be mentioned here is quite a common one: if the threaded spindle is too thin, it may distort (kink) to one side.

A few piston tank designs

$$d_{min} = \sqrt{\frac{F \times S \times 64 \times L}{31 \times E \times 1000}}$$

where

d_{min}: Spindle core diameter in m (approx. 0.8 × nominal diameter)
S: Safety factor (in this case 5 to 10)
L: Free length of spindle in mm
E Modulus of elasticity in N/m²
210 . 10{9} for steel
104 . 10{9} for brass

End-point switches must be fitted to break the power circuit, otherwise the piston will run against the cylinder cap at the end of its stroke and cause damage to the mechanics or motor. To ensure that the piston can return from its final position, the end-point switches should be bridged by diodes of suitable rating.

An alternative solution – really circumventing the problem altogether – is to design the mechanics in such a way that the motor is simply stalled at the end-point. A

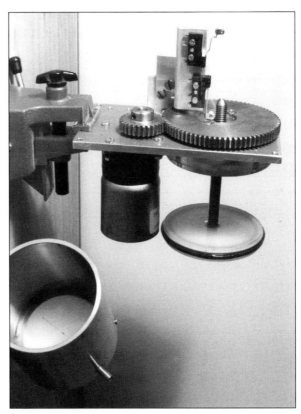

Simple but precision-made piston tank from Helmut Huhn's U5

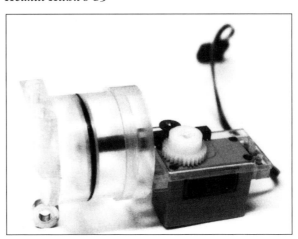

Small diving cells – in this case 20cc capacity for the "Red October" plastic model – can be operated by a powerful servo

properly adjusted proportional control system will then ensure that motor current does not flow continuously, and the motor will then not overheat and only a small current will flow. This system is not as safe or reliable as one featuring end-point switches, and could give rise to problems if radio interference or an electrical fault occurred.

Proportional control systems

Nowadays all our radio control systems are fully proportional, which means that a particular stick deflection

MINI PISTON TANK FOR "RED OCTOBER" PLASTIC MODEL:

V:	20.0	ccm		D:	30.0	mm	
				L:	28.3	mm	
p:	0.3	bar	➜	T:	1.5	s	
				P mech:	0.4	W	
eta g/box:	0.5						
eta mot:	0.5		➜	P el:	1.6	W	
	F piston:	21.2	N				
	d min:	2.4	mm	(Made of V2A [type of stainless steel])			

PISTON TANK FOR "PERFUSOR" SYRINGE:

V:	50.0	ccm		D:	30.0	mm	
				L:	70.8	mm	
p:	0.8	bar	➜	T:	10.0	s	
				P mech:	0.4	W	
eta g/box:	0.5						
eta mot:	0.5		➜	P el:	1.6	W	
	F piston:	56.5	N				
	d min:	3.8	mm	(Made of V2A [type of stainless steel])			
h:	15.7	mm		Rack m = 0.5			
				Pinion 10-tooth			
n Empty:	8000.0	Upm	➜	i:	148.0		
				Corresponds to sailwinch			

PISTON TANK FOR "FORELLE" OR AS A CONTROL TANK FOR BOATS AROUND 10KG:

V:	100.0	ccm		D:	50.0	mm	
				L:	51.0	mm	
p:	0.8	bar	➜	T:	10.0	s	
				P el:	0.8	W	
eta g/box:	0.5						
eta mot:	0.5		➜	P el:	3.2	W	
				Make	2233		
	F piston:	157.0	N				
	d min:	4.5	mm	(Made of V2A [type of stainless steel])			
h:	1.0	mm		Pulley spindle M6			
n Empty:	8000.0	Upm	➜	i:	13.1		

PISTON TANK OF 250 CC VOLUME:

V:	250.0	ccm		D:	70.0	mm	
				L:	65.0	mm	
p:	0.8	bar	➜	T:	20.0	s	
				P mech:	1.0	W	
eta g/box:	0.1						
eta mot:	0.5		➜	P el:	20.0	W	
				Buehler-Motor (Make of motor) 12 V/1.8A			
	F piston:	307.0	N				
	d min:	5.7	mm	(Made of V2A [type of stainless steel])			
h:	1.00	mm		Standard M6 thread			
n Empty:	13600.0	Upm	➜	i:	34.9		

PISTON TANK OF 500 CC VOLUME:

V:	500.0	ccm		D:	70.0	mm
				L:	130.0	mm
p:	0.8	bar		T:	20.0	s
			➜	P mech:	2.0	W
eta g/box:	0.1					
eta mot:	0.5		➜	P el:	40.0	W
	F piston:	307.7	N			
	d min:	6.8	mm	(Made of V2A [type of stainless steel])		
h:	1.25	mm		Standard M8 thread		
n Empty:	10000.0	Upm	➜	i:	16.0	

PISTON TANK OF 1.5l VOLUME:

V:	1500.0	ccm		D:	80.0	mm
				L:	298.6	mm
p:	0.8	bar		T:	40.0	s
			➜	P mech:	3.0	W
eta g/box:	0.1					
eta mot:	0.5		➜	P el:	60.0	W!!
	F piston:	401.9	N			
	d min:	8.9	mm	(Made of V2A [type of stainless steel])		
h:	1.5	mm		Standard M10 thread		
n Empty:	8000.0	Upm	➜	i:	13.4	

PISTON TANK FOR LARGE BOATS OF MORE THAN 25KG DISPLACEMENT:

V:	2500.0	ccm		D:	100.0	mm
				L:	318.5	mm
p:	0.8	bar		T:	40.0	s
			➜	P mech:	5.0	W
eta g/box:	0.1					
eta mot:	0.5		➜	P el:	100.0	W
	F piston:	628.0	N			
	d min:	10.1	mm	(Made of V2A [type of stainless steel])		
h:	1.5	mm		Standard M12 thread		
n Empty:	8000.0	Upm	➜	i:	12.6	

at the transmitter corresponds to a certain servo deflection in the model. In practice the servo simply follows the movement of the transmitter stick. Centre position equals centre position, end-point equals end-point, and all intermediate stick positions are reproduced exactly by the servo.

That is simply what we all expect today, but it was a huge advance at the time of its introduction for those of us accustomed to "bang-bang" control. At that time you were fortunate if you had two buttons for each control surface: one button press caused the servo motor to run in one direction and turn the control surface, and when you released it it would either stop where it was, or – if you had exotic self-neutralising servos – returned to centre. Even with this crude system a sufficiently skilled modeller could fly quite accurate aerobatic manoeuvres with his model aircraft or guide his boat round complex courses.

When you think about it, we only actually use proportional control for our boats' control surfaces and motors. For all the other functions we screw a pair of micro-switches to the servo and go straight back to the old bang-bang days, except that now everything is technically more complex.

In those "good old days" even our servos were often home-made – and this is still possible today. Of course, our servos are now fitted with electronic circuitry – not the case then – but that should not scare us off.

A servo consists of four basic sub-assemblies: motor, gearbox, feedback potentiometer and electronics. The feedback pot is connected to the output (usually a lever or disc) and converts the output shaft's position into an electrical signal – usually a voltage. The servo electronics convert this voltage into a signal which can be compared with the receiver signal, itself determined by the stick position at the transmitter.

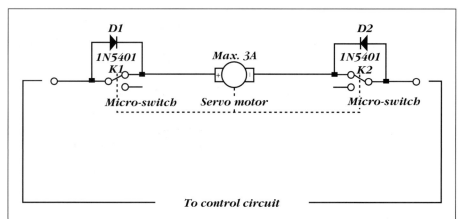

Regardless of the method of control it is important to install end-point switches to protect the diving cell motor from being stalled at the end-points

If the two signals are of equal length, the servo is in the right position and no current is fed to the servo motor. If one of the two is longer, then current is passed to the motor. The motor moves the pot (and with it the output shaft) to the point where equilibrium is regained. If the stick is moved, the associated pulse length (often termed "pulse width") changes and the electronic circuit controls the motor until the new position is reached. The servo (lat. servus: servant) follows the stick movement.

There is a second way in which a difference may occur between the transmitter's signal and the pot's signal: this occurs when an external force moves the servo output. The motor is again set in motion and the deviation is corrected. Thus although an external force will affect the servo, the effect is temporary, and the servo compensates for it.

We don't really need to worry about the electronics, as the circuit is a ready-made item which we buy. The circuit is basically the same for all servos of standard size, regardless of their mechanical construction. Some model companies sell standard servo electronics individually, designed for 4.8V motors drawing up to 500 mA (Conrad Electronic No. 23 49 07 – 44).

If more power is required than an ordinary servo can supply, we need to look elsewhere – but not far away. Standard commercial speed controllers will do the job. Speed controllers consist of perfectly normal servo electronics combined with an output stage which is capable of processing the high currents involved. The main difference is that the feedback pot is replaced by a trim pot.

If we look more closely we find that the values for dead time, expansion and internal reverse coupling are also rather different, as the characteristics of ordinary servo electronics are not ideal for the speed controller application.

Since there is no reason why we should not make our own servos, and make them any shape and power we want, it must be worthwhile to consider building a diving cell control system in the form of a servo. In practice this means that a feedback pot has to be installed in some way which registers the position of the piston. This pot is fitted to a speed controller in place of the usual zero trimmer, and the motor is connected to the modified controller. This amounts to a proportionally controlled diving cell, and we will call it a servo diving cell.

The advantage is an appreciable improvement in convenience of control. If a submarine is fitted with a bang-bang control system (a very popular solution) the operator can never know exactly how much water is in his diving cell at any one time. The best he can hope for is to know how long he has allowed the motor to work, and from this he can estimate how full the tank is.

With a servo diving cell the piston position always corresponds to the position of the transmitter slider, so the amount of water in the diving tank is always known. During the first trial run the operator

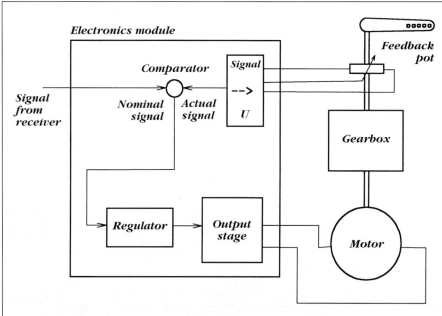

The position of the servo output is determined by a closed regulatory circuit (principle of operation only)

simply marks on the transmitter the correct slider position for constant depth. Any adjustments can be made at any time, and take a matter of moments. If, during the course of a day's running, the operator finds that his boat is sinking when the slider is at the marked position, then he has received a reliable warning that water has got inside the model. Indeed, if he re-trims his boat for constant depth and refers to the new slider position, he can very accurately determine the quantity of water which has got inside.

The precise control conferred by a servo diving cell is also very useful when you want to carry out slow, controlled under-water manoeuvres, and control in general is much easier.

But now let us return to constructing the system: the mechanical system is the same except that it now features a feedback pot. There are at least three types of pot suitable for this purpose:

Bearing in mind the linear travel of the piston the most obvious choice is a linear (slider) potentiometer, although we then find an immediate limitation due to the standard 58mm stroke of these items. Standard servo electronics use roughly a third of this stroke, which equates to a piston travel of around 19mm which would seldom be adequate. However, with the addition of two trim pots we can extend the stroke up to the whole travel of the slider. If we leave a little "spare" travel, this gives us a maximum stroke of about 50mm, and with a piston diameter of 50mm we have a movable volume of about 100cm³.

The second option is to use a conventional 270° rotary pot, in which case we can adjust the linear travel by adjusting the length of the actuating arm. The usual way of using a rotary pot is to employ the central third of the travel (90°), without extending the working range. We now require a lever length of:

Lever length = stroke 0.7

In a typical slim submarine of characteristic elongated cylindrical shape this presents considerable installation problems. However, if there is room for it in the boat, then this is a very practical solution.

It is simple to make and at the same time offers adjustment facilities for stroke (re-connect the pushrod to a different hole) and neutral position (rotate the lever on the pot shaft).

The third alternative involves more complexity, but it also gives the greatest flexibility. This is the spindle potentiometer, encompassing 10-way pots designed for front panel mounting, and spindle trimmers of the 20-or 25-turn type. The pot is connected to the spindle nut via an adaptor gearbox. Since this gearbox can be selected to give any ratio you like,

Linear pot is ideal for registering the position of a 50mm stroke diving cell

it is possible to set exactly the piston stroke you need. The reduction ratio is:

$$i_{pot} = \frac{L}{h \times N_{pot}}$$

where
L: Piston stroke
i_{pot}:   Reduction ratio of pot gearbox
h: Spindle pitch
N_{pot}: Number of pot turns used

If the reduction ratio is higher than 1:10 it is possible to simplify construction considerably by fitting a small gear wheel on the pot shaft, using the spindle as a rack. The matching modulus is h/{pi}, which equates to m0.4 with an M8 spindle or about m0.3 for M6.

The final option is a highly professional system based on an incremental counter attached to the motor shaft, but this requires specialised micro-processor based electronics, and is too complex for modelling purposes.

As already mentioned, a standard speed controller can serve as the electronics for our piston servo, although it will not be quite as accurate as a normal

Attaching a rotary pot to a short-stroke piston tank

With a long-stroke piston tank a spindle and gear can be used (Aeronaut tank)

servo. We have already discussed how end-point switches are fitted in addition to the feedback pot and trim pots. We also need a failsafe circuit in front of the speed controller to ensure that the boat will surface automatically if it dives too deep and radio contact is lost.

Here is a circuit for special servo diving cell electronics which incorporates a number of special features:

The circuit of the NE 544 servo IC is designed expressly for servo use. The feedback pot is controlled by two trim pots providing an adjustment facility for both end-points of the working range. The circuit includes auxiliary connections for the end-point switches, and no diodes are required. However, the most important refinement is an integral signal failure detection circuit (failsafe) which ensures that the diving cell is emptied to the point set by the end-point switch in the event of radio contact failure.

When you are assembling and testing the servo components you may encounter a few problems concerning the polarity of the motor and pot. The only recourse here is to check the system using the transmitter and receiver or a servo tester. If the servo runs to one end-stop when it should be at centre, and it cannot be moved from there by adjusting the trim pot, you need to reverse the polarity of the motor. If that works, but the tank floods instead of being emptied when you switch off the transmitter (failsafe operation), both motor and feedback pot must be reversed (the central connection to the pot is left unchanged).

Compressed air

In military submarines a method of submerging using diving tanks which can be evacuated by compressed air has been in use since the turn of the century. In models of such vessels this is the only really true-scale procedure and it has often been emulated, albeit more often in Holland and England than in Germany, where piston tanks predominate. This is due partly to the availability of

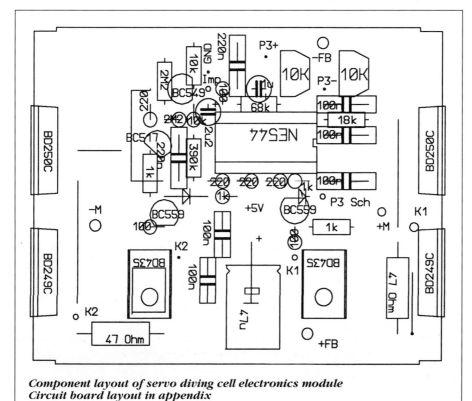

Component layout of servo diving cell electronics module
Circuit board layout in appendix

commercial German-made kits, most of which are fitted with piston tanks, and partly to the widespread understanding of the piston system, which in any case is more suitable for model use in general terms.

Nevertheless: if you are planning a scale model of a military submarine you should at least consider the method used in the full-size vessel, otherwise you are not in a position to make an informed decision.

In a compressed air system the diving tank has openings on its underside connected to the outside water. At the top of the tank there is a flooding valve through which the air escapes when open, with the result that the tank fills through the bottom opening. For submerged running all the air is passed through these valves and they are closed again.

When the sub is to surface, compressed air is blown into the tank via inlet valves, and the water is pushed out again. The compressed air comes from pressure bottles stowed in the submarine.

The greater the depth of the boat, the more air is needed to fill the tanks, as air is highly compressible and is affected by water pressure. At 10m depth, i.e. at a pressure of 1 bar, its volume is reduced by one half. As the boat rises the air expands again as water pressure diminishes, and the excess air leaves the diving tank through the bottom opening in the form of a stream of air bubbles. When the boat is running on the surface a compressor is operated to refill the pressure bottles.

Full-size boats are fitted with a large number of diving cells each with its own valves. This increases the safety level in case of damage, and permits accurate control of the diving process. An additional pressurised control cell with its own bottom valve is also installed to allow accurate control of the constant depth setting and to compensate for differences in weight. The control cell is also used when the boat is required to manoeuvre slowly. Two further trim cells of similar type are fitted in the bow and stern so that the submarine's fore-and-aft trim can be adjusted, i.e. the longitudinal distribution of weight. Under normal circumstances these three cells are kept partially filled – the only ones to which this applies.

For model use it is also advisable to install a control cell in the form of a piston tank, together with a movable ballast trimming mechanism. In fact virtually all submarine modellers manage perfectly well without these refinements, and run their boats with a little residual air in the diving tanks which is usually sufficient to cope with the submarine's usual manoeuvres.

Unfortunately this small quantity of residual air is compressed as the boat dives, so buoyancy is lost and the vessel tends to sink increasingly quickly. However, the usual depths at which models run is no more than a few metres, so the loss of volume is as slight as the increase in pressure, whereas this is not the case with full-size vessels. Even so, this is an inherent drawback, and the method cannot provide accurate control of constant depth.

For a practical implementation there is no alternative but to fall back on the range of products made by specialist pneumatics manufacturers (see appendix), assuming that you can and want to afford the outlay. I can highly recommend the Festo range of micro-pneumatics for modelling use, as the parts are so compact that they can be accommodated in quite small models. They are also cheaper than conventional systems.

All of your model submarine's pipework, air valves and throttles, pressure reducers and switches and even the snorkel valve can be assembled from these ready-made parts which are readily available.]

The pressure difference at the flooding valve is very small, as it represents only the difference in water level between the diving cell and the outside water, which amounts to just a few mbar (1cm water column is roughly 1mbar). This applies when the tank is empty, but of course it falls off as the tank is flooded since the water level is then rising in the diving cell.

To achieve realistic diving times the flooding valve must be of much larger cross-section than is possible with magnetic valves unless they are servo-assisted. The actual valve of a servo-assisted magnetic valve is actuated by compressed air controlled by a small magnet-operated supplementary valve. However, since there is no separate connection for the supplementary air, the flooding valve would not open at all since the excess pressure in the diving cell is too slight to trigger it. The right sort of special-purpose valves are, in fact, available, as they are used in steam ironing tables (see appendix). Alternatively we can consider building our own servo-operated valves – as already explained in connection with pump-operated tanks. In this case the micro-switch used for the pump is replaced by a micro piston valve of the same size, working as the air inlet valve. In this case it is necessary to carry out the minor task of closing off the vent opening "R" using silicone sealant.

The final option is to install undersized pneumatic valves, and learn to be patient when flooding the tank. Annoying queries from spectators can be countered with the information that things have to go that slowly in order to be true to scale.

In valve manufacturers' catalogues the unit of throughput resistance is stated as the standard nominal throughflow. This refers to the volumetric throughflow corrected for normal temperature and pressure (1.013 bar, 0° C) with a pressure loss of 1 bar and an excess input pressure of 6 bar. These are realistic figures for normal pneumatic usage, but for our purposes they have to be corrected:

$$Q = Q_n \left(\frac{p}{p_n} \right)^{1.5} \times \left(\frac{D_p}{D_{pn}} \right)^{0.5}$$

where

Q: Throughflow in l/min
p: Absolute pressure in bar
D_p: Pressure difference in bar
p_n: Nominal pressure 6.5 bar
D_{pn}: Nominal pressure difference 1 bar

Example: with a ⅛" 2/2 travel valve (the largest direct-acting type) and a height difference of 10cm:

$$Q = 300 \ \text{l/min} \ \left(\frac{1}{6.5} \right)^{1.5} \left(\frac{0.01}{1} \right)^{0.5} = 1.8 \ \text{l/min}$$

Using this figure we can estimate the flooding time Tflut for a diving tank of volume VTt = 1

$$T_{flut} = \frac{V_{Tt}}{Q} = 33s$$

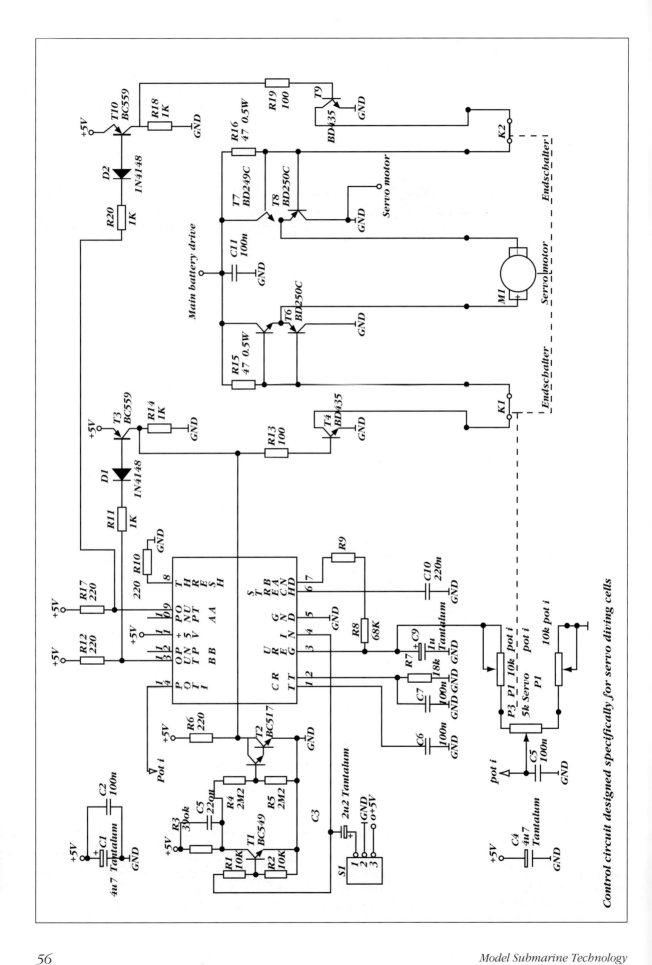

Control circuit designed specifically for servo diving cells

If you bear in mind the time scale (square root of linear scale) this is very slow indeed.

As you can see, the vertical difference between the two water levels is important here, in addition to the flow resistance of the valve. The diving tank should therefore be located as low as possible in the boat in order to obtain reasonably fast flooding. At the same time you must ensure that the tank is not excessively long, otherwise the exposed water surface in the partially filled tank will be large, and you can expect stability problems.

The air inlet hose also incorporates a pressure reducer and a throttle in addition to the valve, to allow adjustment of the air inflow speed. Without a throttle the tank would be blown completely full of air in a fraction of a second.

On the one hand this is highly non-scale and deprives the operator of fine control over the quantity of ballast water retained, and on the other it would rapidly overload the diving tank, since the bottom opening is usually not large enough for the water to flow out at such a high speed. Excess pressure then

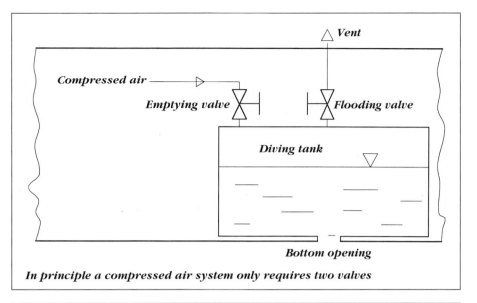

In principle a compressed air system only requires two valves

Valves

builds up in the tank, and it can even reach the same pressure as the air reservoir. However, the diving tank is only designed to withstand water pressure at the design diving depth (i.e. maximum 10m, corresponding to 1 bar), and this places the submarine in acute danger.

The pressure reducer valve is not an absolute necessity, but it does prevent a disaster if, say, the bottom opening should become blocked – something which does indeed occur from time time and against which the throttle offers no protection.

The pressure reducer valve is set to a pressure corresponding to the maximum diving depth plus a small safety margin. A pleasant side-effect is that the air inlet speed stays constant, instead of varying according to the pressure in the air bottle, which is constantly changing.

A central problem with this type of system is how to store the compressed air in the model. In full-size

submarines special high-pressure steel vessels are used, distributed throughout the boat, operating at pressures of around 200 bar. In our models the pressure is much lower – around 6 bar – which means that the storage tanks take up much more space.

Their volume can be calculated as follows:

$$V_{sp} = \frac{V_{Tauch} \times n_{gang}}{(1 + P_{ws})P_{sp}}$$

. where:

V_{sp}:   Volume of storage vessel in dm^3
V_{Tauch}: Volume of diving cell in dm^3
n_{gang}:   Number of possible dives
p_{sp}:   Pressure of storage vessel in bar
p_{ws}:   Water pressure at design diving depth in bar

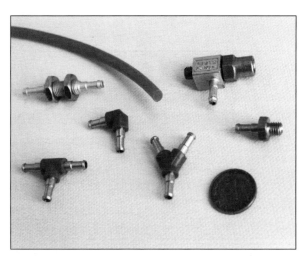

Connectors and junctions

Under realistic operational conditions (i.e. not always blowing the tanks completely at maximum diving depth) a far greater number of dives is possible. For this reason the value for Ngang used in the calculation does not need to be very high. Without an on-board compressor a value of at least 8-10 is advisable, but if an on-board compressor is present, a figure as low as 2-3 is sufficient.

For a typical boat, e.g. a 1:40 scale VIIc U-boat, the result is as follows:

$$\frac{1.5\,\mathrm{l} \times 10}{(1 + 0.8\,\mathrm{bar})8\,\mathrm{bar}} = 1.041$$

or 0.3 l with an on-board compressor.

Since a pressure tank represents a very serious hazard if overloaded or of faulty construction, these tanks must be treated with special care. If you have ever dabbled in steam engines you will already know this: the strength of the boiler (in our case the pressure tank) has to be calculated and tested with the actual vessel under test conditions. Pressure vessels with a pressure litre product below 200 bar dm≥ are exempt from official test regulations [in Germany]. For a detailed description of the test procedures please refer to the specialist literature relating to model steam engines.

The only shape of container which is permissible is a cylinder with cambered ends, even though they are not as easy to accommodate as rectangular shapes. The necessary wall thickness is found as follows:

$$S_{min} = \frac{D_i \times p_{sp} \times S \times 10^5}{2K}$$

where

S_{min}: Minimum wall thickness in mm
D_i: Internal diameter in mm
p_{sp}: Internal pressure in bar
S: Safety factor, e.g. 8
K: Elastic limit of the material in N/mm²

Minimum strength of standard commercial materials:
Copper: 180 Nmm²
Steel St37: 235 Nmm²

The ends should be as highly curved as possible since flat sheets are almost incapable of withstanding pressure loads. Reinforcements are necessary around the pipe openings unless the wall thickness of the tank is very generous. Highly corrosion-resistant pressure tanks in many shapes and sizes can be made from standard commercial copper pipe and matching end caps provided that the joints are silver-soldered.

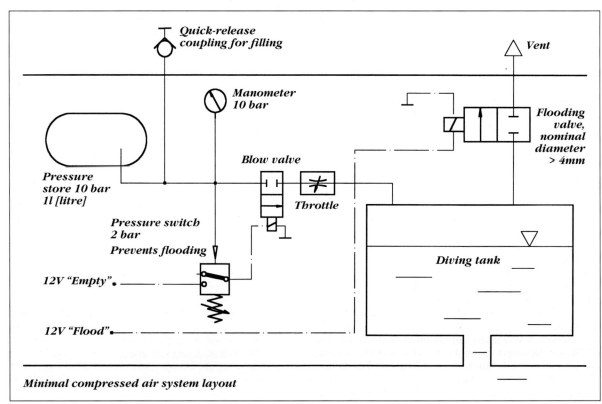

Minimal compressed air system layout

If steel pipe is used all joints must be welded, and this is often outside the modeller's capabilities, although many a local car repair shop will be happy to help you. Since steel pipe is usually only available in wall thicknesses of 2.5mm and more, this material can only be recommended for large tanks (several litres) in any case.

A large number of ready-made pressure tanks is available commercially. One type we can recommend is sold as an oxygen cartridge for hobby soldering apparatus, some of which are approved for pressures up to 35 bar.

Other pressure vessels can be found which are intended for one-shot usage, but even so the maximum permissible pressure is often printed on them. However, they are not always straightforward to use since the very thin, highly stressed walls must not be drilled, and therefore only the original opening can be used. Another problem is that condensate will always collect in the pressure tank, and this can lead to corrosion. Of course, the thinner the wall, the faster it rusts through.

Compressed air can either be produced externally or inside the submarine itself. If you are satisfied with an external source all you need is a simple air pump designed for inflating car or bicycle tyres. Modellers less keen on physical exertion may prefer to use a 12-volt compressor from the DIY store.

However, this type of compressor can also be installed directly in the boat since electric power is available, even if there is no crew to operate the machine. Not that switching an on-board compressor on and off presents too many problems. The obvious advantage is that the maximum running time of the model is now determined by battery capacity, and you don't need to bring the boat back to the shore continually to replenish the air tank.

The 12V compressor mentioned above is not very large provided that you remove it from the casing. These units are powered by a direct-drive Mabuchi 550 electric motor, and unfortunately they vibrate extremely badly and are very noisy in operation. These aspects of the compressor's performance can be improved by installing a different motor, e.g. a car heater fan motor. The compressor should be mounted on very resilient rubber buffers to isolate the hull from the vibration.

An automatic air inlet valve must be provided in the boat to give the compressor the air it needs to inhale during surface running. One idea is to use a gooseneck with a float to seal the end, or a magnetic valve with a float switch. The valve is fitted in the pipe between a short snorkel inside the turret which leads to the boat's internal cavity. The compressor then sucks air out of this space.

Of course, it is possible for the compressor to be fed outside air through the snorkel, which would allow the the boat's main cavity to be kept hermetically sealed. In this case a special water separator must be incorporated in the pipeline.

It is worth noting that any extensive pneumatic system inside a model submarine involves the danger that minor leaks will pressurise the internal cavity over a period of time, and this could eventually cause damage to the hull.

However, if you allow the compressor to suck air out of the cavity, any tension in the hull will be released every time the sub surfaces, and there will also be a slight ventilation effect. In this case the bilges function as water separator for droplets of moisture that may have been picked up. This process more or less corresponds to the full-size system. If you really want to "go to town", you could always install an extending snorkel through which the compressor could suck air when the boat is running at snorkel depth.

Whatever the system you choose, a pressure switch must be fitted to turn off the compressor when the required pressure is reached. This item is also available as a component of standard pneumatic systems. You could even make your own one consisting of a manometer and a "light beam" which can "read" the manometer needle. Another absolutely essential refinement in any system which does not include an on-board compressor is an extra pressure switch which prevents the flooding valve opening if there is insufficient pressure to blow out the tank subsequently.

Another quite different method of ensuring that there is always enough "air" available to fill the diving tank is to use liquid gas. Since the gas is stored in its dense liquid form, a small pressure tank can hold sufficient gas for many dives. There are four gases from which to choose:

- Difluoro-dichloro-methane in compressed form is sold under the trade name "Frigen" for airbrushes and car air horns. It is non-flammable and non-toxic to humans, but it does damage the ozone layer, and that is reason enough not to use it. A replacement product is now on sale which is said to be non-injurious.

- Butane is much cheaper and more environmentally friendly, but it is highly inflammable. If it is mixed with air it may explode. For this reason it must not be used in a submarine unless you can be 100% certain that the gas cannot possibly leak into the model's main cavity.

An interesting English design achieves this goal by installing the gas tank and the blow valve inside the diving tank. If a leak occurs, the diving tank fills with gas, and provided that the boat is watertight no gas can reach the main cavity. Even so, the system still represents a fire hazard when setting it up on land.

- Carbon dioxide is neither inflammable nor environmentally harmful (at least not in the quantities which we are likely to use), but unfortunately it only liquifies at a pressure of 60 bar, which calls for the use of a high-pressure gas bottle and a suitable pressure reducer. Small carbon dioxide bottles are available, designed for pressurised drinks, and thus they are quite easy to obtain, albeit relatively expensive. The bottles must be vertical when gas is removed otherwise the valve will ice up. Viewed overall carbon dioxide presents too many problems for most modellers.

- If air is compressed at 200 bar it still does not liquefy, but even so a large quantity of gas can then be stored in quite a small volume. 1 litre bottles of compressed air are manufactured for divers. Naturally they are somewhat more expensive to buy, and they do require a special pressure reducer. The compensation is that a single fill will yield up to 50 dives. For a small fee any underwater diving club will re-fill the bottle for you.

Compressor

The great advantage of a compressed air system is that you don't need a lathe or an engineering workshop, because virtually all the components can be bought "off the shelf". At the same time this represents the system's principle drawback: the components have industrial price tags, and are therefore relatively expensive for the private individual.

In its most basic form a compressed air system is the simplest solution to many model submarine problems. Even when fully expanded, with an on-board compressor, inlet valve and multiple diving tanks, the system may well be extremely complex but it is still easy to

understand and maintain. If you intend building large submarines, a compressed air system can easily handle the large quantities of ballast water you will need to move.

Once a boat is fitted with a compressed air system, it can be used to power other auxiliary functions too. Periscopes and snorkels can be run in and out via double-acting pneumatic cylinders and 4-way valves, and even folding hydroplanes can be implemented. If you really want to get involved in pneumatics, there is no reason why you should not construct pneumatic servos for the rudder and hydroplanes.

One aspect of diving tanks which has not yet been mentioned is this: in principle all the diving tanks which we have discussed, including those based on compressed air systems, can be controlled proportionally. This involves installing a sensor which detects when the tank is full. The sensor should be designed in such a way that it is not influenced by other disturbances such as roll or pitch movements.

A suitable system would be a 270° potentiometer with a lever 0.7 x tank height in length, together with a float. A suitable electronic circuit then controls the flooding and air inlet valves in accordance with any difference between the nominal and actual levels in the diving tank. So much for the theory. In practice the water slapping about and the compressibility of the air present quite a number of problems which do not arise with the piston tank. In general terms a control circuit – for example, a servo control system – is the more accurate and simple, the more direct is the connection between the command signal and the resultant actual value.

I have never heard of a servo diving tank which is not based on a piston tank, but don't let that stop you. If you are experimentally minded, the whole field is open to you.

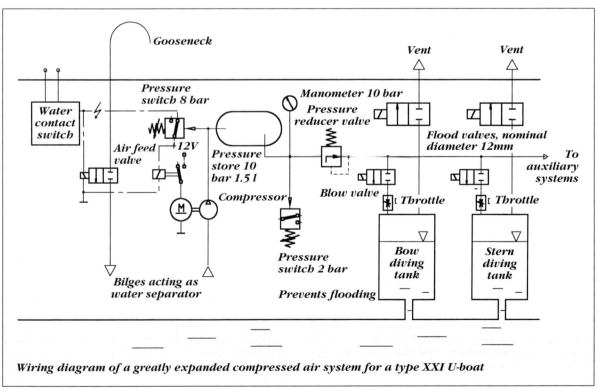

Wiring diagram of a greatly expanded compressed air system for a type XXI U-boat

Chapter 7

Trim Mechanisms

The purpose of a trim mechanism is to allow the operator to alter the submarine's centre of mass, in order to to tilt the model around its lateral axis – even when at rest. Nose down in the water, tail in the air, and down we go into the depths. Every now and then you may even need to reverse this manoeuvre in order to surface when a hydroplane gets jammed on a twig.

Many submarines – including research machines and the "Brandtaucher" of 1850 – manoeuvre entirely by means of movable ballast, and do not use hydroplanes at all. In any case hydroplanes would have little significant effect when the vessel is moving at low speed, as required for observation work close to the bottom. A great advantage to us is that a radio-controlled trim mechanism eliminates the need to trim the model accurately in the first place. Provided that the boat is adjusted to a more or less level attitude we don't need to worry about the last degree or two. The fine-tuning is carried out by giving the appropriate transmitter lever a little push. The extra effort in installing the trim system is paid back in the course of the model's life, as you can easily adjust the boat's trim if you make some minor change to its technology (such as trying out a different speed controller). Otherwise you will need to carry out a series of bathtub tests every time you make a change, to ensure that the lead ballast is in the correct position.

Multiple diving tanks

One popular method of weight shifting is to install two diving tanks – one in the bow and one in the stern. Partially flooding the one and simultaneously emptying the other shifts the vessel's centre of gravity.

The main problem with this method is that of controlling the tanks accurately. If you have sufficiently accurate proportional control the system can work really well. Initial trials will establish the transmitter slider settings for constant depth, and minor adjustments are made to obtain the correct horizontal attitude. Marks can then be made against the sliders so that the positions can be found again relatively easily. You can even make these adjustments while the submarine is moving.

However, if you flood or empty the tanks by mistake you have to go to the bother of re-trimming the constant depth settings and then the horizontal attitude, and this can take a little while. Every time you make an adjustment you have to let the boat settle in order to check the results of your efforts. Accurate settings for constant depth are a fundamental necessity if you want your sub to manoeuvre accurately when submerged, so it is particularly important to be able to trim the model very accurately.

If you are just slightly lucky the boat will remain horizontal when both flooding valves are operated for the same length of time. However, if you wish to tilt the boat whilst keeping it at a constant depth, the problems are almost insurmountable.

Ballast shifting

For this reason it makes a lot of sense to separate the two functions of diving tank and trimming, and make them independent of each other. Trim cells are often used in large military submarines and many research submarines, and ballast (water or mercury) is pumped to and fro between them to adjust the vessel's longitudinal trim. This principle can also be implemented in a model.

Far less space-consuming for our purpose, as well as being simpler to control, is a system involving the movement of fixed ballast, and this type of system is also used in some small research submarines. The obvious item of fixed ballast in our case is the main drive battery.

We can calculate the angle of inclination which can be obtained by weight shift as follows:

$$\alpha = \arctan \frac{b \times m_{schieb}}{MZH \times m_{ges}}$$

where
α: Pitch-axis angle in degrees
b: Linear shift of ballast in mm
m_{schieb}: Mass of ballast in kg
MZH: Metacentric height in mm
m_{ges}:   Total mass of boat in kg

The linear travel required is only a few cm, and the larger the proportion of the ballast relative to the boat's total weight, the smaller the travel required. For example, if your model weights 15kg and has a metacentric height of 10mm (typical figures for a VIIc U-boat built to 1:40 scale) a 20° angle of tilt is obtained by moving a 3kg weight by 18mm.

The first requirement for a working implementation is that the battery must be mounted in such a way that it can slide forward and aft, but not laterally or vertically. A proven solution is to glue the battery to a pair of guide tubes which can then slide along a pair of fixed rods. If you are using NiCd batteries you can hold the pack and the tubes together with heat-shrink sleeving.

Bearing in mind the short travel and reasonable forces a low-speed servo will usually be able to cope in smaller boats. Modern servos have enough power to push the ballast weight vertically. This will give an adequate reserve of power for most model submarines, enabling the servo to cope with tilt angles around 30° plus a little friction. If you are not sure of a servo's power you should refer to the manufacturer's catalogue.

One danger is that the servo might be damaged by shock load if the model sub rams an unseen obstacle. True, nobody in their right mind would deliberately run a boat into a concrete wall at full speed, but there are a good many under-water obstacles which are hard to see and which have exactly the same effect. If your submarine suffers such a collision with little or no damage, then that is a credit to your building skills, and the model will probably have a long and enjoyable life.

Nevertheless a ballast shifting system does require some form of buffer against shock damage, and this takes the form of a servo-saver, as they are known in their normal world – that of model cars. The shock is absorbed by a spring in the mechanism.

In larger boats you will have to build a high-power servo yourself in order to shift the ballast, and you can then design the mechanism to be inherently shock-absorbing. For example, you could base the servo on a standard threaded spindle.

Although these systems are characterised by low efficiency, they are inherently self-locking and absorb any shock load themselves, i.e. they do not transmit the force to the gearbox and motor. The spindle and its mounting must be designed to withstand the considerable forces involved, but this does not present major difficulties.

An alternative solution is to move the ballast by a belt wrapped round a pulley, held under tension by a spring. If the system is overloaded the belt simply slips on the pulley, thereby isolating the gearbox and motor from the shock. Since the feedback pot is moved directly by the ballast, the ballast can only be in the wrong position for a short while as the servo electronics immediately correct the deviation by switching the motor on.

The speed of the trim mechanism should be in the range 1 to 10 seconds, but it is not very critical since the boat responds very slowly in any case. As long as the trim mechanism can work faster than the boat's natural rate of pitch-axis movement, then it will have no negative influence on the submarine's control characteristics. If you only intend using the trim system to carry out a once-and-for-all adjustment of the boat's horizontal attitude, and not to control the vessel, the speed of the trim mechanism is of no account, and it can be as slow as you like.

The size and power of the servo motor can be calculated using the same formula as for a piston tank:

$$0.5 I_{max} \times U = P_{elek} = \frac{P_{max} \times 0.0000785 \times D^2 \times L}{T_{stell} \times eta_{getr} \times eta_{mot}}$$

where
I_{max}:   Stall current in A
U: Voltage in V
P_{elek}:   Motor power in W
M: Mass to be moved in kg
g: Gravitational constant 9.81m/s²
L: Stroke in mm
T_{stell}:   Speed of travel in sec.
eta_{getr}:   Efficiency of gearbox + spindle

0.1 for standard thread
0.5 for belt, rack, special spindles

eta_{mot}:   Motor efficiency
(at this power level; not maximum efficiency)

The reduction ratio required is then:

$$i = \frac{n_{max} \times h}{120 \times T_{stell} \times L}$$

where
n_{max}:   No-load speed in rpm
h: Pitch of spindle or periphery of pulley in mm
i: Reduction ratio

Servo saver

Chapter 8

Trimming

You don't want your first trial dive to end in disaster, do you? To give the boat a reasonable chance of success and to give you a fair probability of seeing it on the surface again, it is essential to trim it out very carefully beforehand. Accurate trim at constant depth with the diving cells flooded is one precondition for successful operation, and the second is correct – i.e. horizontal – attitude.

Even a trim error of a few degrees forces the land-based operator to keep the hydroplanes constantly in motion to compensate. Even if he is able to hold the boat level he will probably be quite unable to steer the model.

Unfortunately this initial trimming is a very laborious business: you place the boat in the water, flood the diving cell (s), assess the vessel's attitude, then lift it out of the bathtub again. Open it up, add or remove ballast then close it again. This is one moment when you realise the value of a fast and efficient hull seal mechanism. You can expect to repeat this process a dozen times until you achieve an attitude which is at least approximately correct.

If you now take the trouble to stow and fix the ballast properly, you can start on the fine-tuning work using small trim weights. Balance weights designed for aluminium car wheels are helpful here: the weight is printed on them, and the self-adhesive strip makes them easy to fix. You can speed up this phase considerably by placing the weights on the deck until you achieve a reliable horizontal attitude when submerged. Once you are satisfied, install all the weights inside the hull in one process.

During this whole procedure it is important to keep in mind the model's inherent weight stability, which is a function of the metacentric height, as already discussed. At the trimming stage it is possible to alter the metacentric height significantly by installing the ballast either high up or low down in the hull.

Chapter 9

Depth Regulators

After months of puzzling and struggling with all the details, the great day finally arrives: it's time to submerge the boat for the first time. Even the experienced modeller usually feels a little anxious as he prepares to expose to public scrutiny his ability as a test pilot. Carefully he opens the throttle and his boat picks up speed; even more carefully he starts the diving manoeuvre. The reward for all his work is that the boat disappears, leaving behind a diminishing wake on the surface.

At first you will be absolutely thrilled that it has all worked, but it is not long before the truth dawns: your boat may already be a little too far down, it is already difficult to see, and it is time to regain control of things. Violent hydroplane manoeuvres and emptying of the diving cell bring the model shooting back to the surface like a cork. That's strange: the initial diving procedure was much more majestic . . .

Don't be put off. Anything worthwhile has to be learned, and you can expect to spend the next few weeks practising regularly until you feel properly in control. Round about this stage you will realise that the idea of running your model along the river at periscope depth for a kilometre or more may not be quite as easy as you imagined. After a while you may well manage to keep your boat under control at low speed over a distance of 50m or so without either banging into the bottom or leaping up to the surface; anything better than that just seems impossible.

The crucial reason behind this difficulty is that the operator is always standing on dry land, and his perception of the model's depth at any time is very approximate. Refraction at the water's surface makes the boat's depth appear to vary depending on the distance between operator and model. Sometimes it may even be completely invisible due to the cloudy water. Other factors also have to be considered. As its speed rises the submarine shows an increasing tendency to deviate from the set depth. Even more alarming is that it maintains its heading even when the hydroplanes have been returned

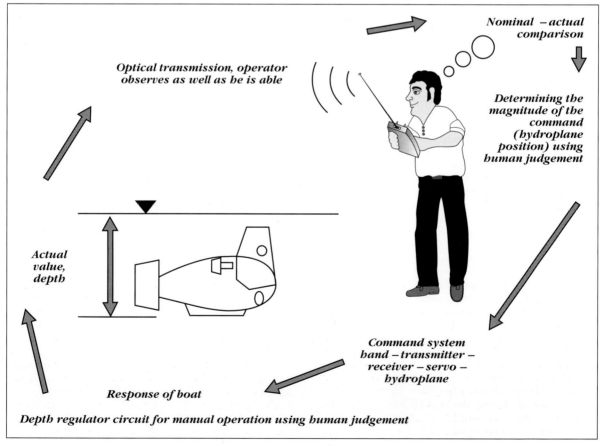

Optical transmission, operator observes as well as he is able

Nominal – actual comparison

Determining the magnitude of the command (hydroplane position) using human judgement

Actual value, depth

Command system hand – transmitter – receiver – servo – hydroplane

Response of boat

Depth regulator circuit for manual operation using human judgement

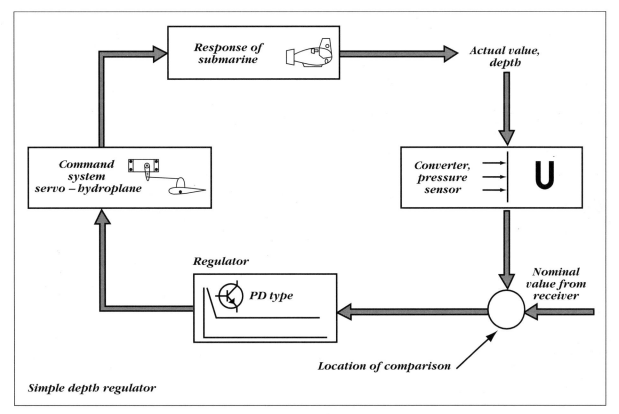

Simple depth regulator

Labels in figure:
Response of submarine — Actual value, depth — Converter, pressure sensor — **U** — Command system servo – hydroplane — Nominal value from receiver — Regulator — PD type — Location of comparison

to neutral. Once the boat has submerged you find you have to use the hydroplanes to get it back to the correct attitude, i.e. horizontal. This is very difficult to see, and just as difficult to do.

When the submarine is stationary or running at low speed, it pitches back to the horizontal very quickly when the hydroplanes are centred. This is a result of the boat's inherent weight stability. With increasing speed the dynamic forces caused by the water flowing over the hull and hydroplanes take over, and they determine what happens subsequently. The force of gravity is proportionately much less significant – if it has any effect at all – and thus is only able to move the boat very slowly.

The only option for the operator is to dive at low speed, so that the boat does actually rotate back to the horizontal as a result of its weight stability. Curious observers and those annoying modelling colleagues of yours can be told imperiously that the submarine is practising furtive running, and showing off typical submarine stalking methods in a highly scale manner.

Of course, research submarines are optimised for maximum manoeuvrability at low speed, and this type of operation is indeed correct for them. In any case these vessels are not generally fitted with the powerful motors which would allow them to run at high speed. Operating this type of boat is therefore extremely straightforward even when the vessel is submerged. With military submarines and some civilian vessels this does not apply; manoeuvring slowly is only one option, and others include high-speed under-water running, both completely submerged and at snorkel depth.

Depth control turned out to be a considerable problem with full-size U-boats when faster and faster boats were developed during the second World War. The solution then was one which had already been developed: automatic depth regulators for torpedoes. These

mechanisms were installed in the first experimental boats virtually unchanged, but they were subsequently superseded by new types developed to meet the new requirements.

Ready-made solutions of this type are unfortunately not available to the model submariner. The only factory-made systems which can be used as a basis for attitude regulators are the expensive gyro systems used to stabilise model helicopters, and even then the results are not that good.

The principle

If we want to use a depth regulator there is little option but to build it, but we can't do that unless we first understand how these systems work.

Let's start by returning to our model submarine operator trying to control his model manually. What he needs to control above all is the submarine's depth. He measures the actual depth at any moment by screwing up his eyes and furrowing his brow. He compares the estimated depth with the nominal depth (the depth he actually wants the submarine to be) and selects a hydroplane setting which he hopes will correct the difference between the two. He pushes a stick, and the deviation is transmitted to the hydroplanes via the radio control system. The boat responds more or less directly to this command, and the actual value (the sub's depth) changes. The whole process represents a cyclic procedure, or loop.

Unfortunately there are two weak points in this regulatory cycle: on the one hand "look and guess" is a very inadequate method of determining the actual value (the boat's depth) at any one time, and on the other the hydroplane setting which he hopes will be right is unlikely to be the ideal one for achieving the desired

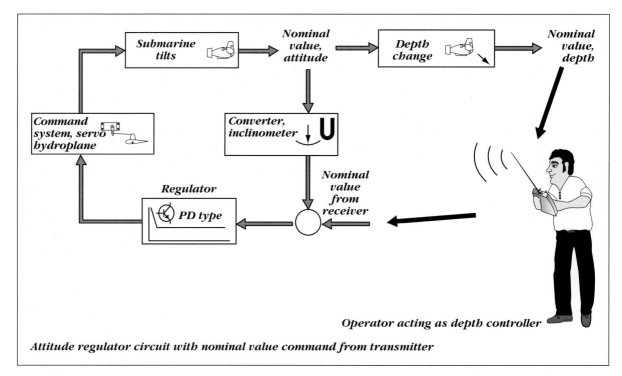

Operator acting as depth controller

Attitude regulator circuit with nominal value command from transmitter

result – at least until he has gathered some experience and confidence.

In both these respects matters are easier for the crew members of a full-size submarine: the crew has a manometer or similar measuring device which tells them the submarine's depth accurately. The full-size boat also responds much more slowly to any command (that time scale again!), giving the crew much more time to make the correct decision.

To sum up: the model submarine operator standing on dry land is clearly unable to regulate his model's submerged depth. This task needs to be assigned to an electronic or mechanical regulator installed in the boat.

In fact, the different aspects of the procedure remain the same. The actual value ("depth") is gauged by a measuring device and converted into a signal which can be processed – for example, an electrical voltage. The voltage is compared to the nominal depth, which is also present in the form of an electrical voltage, having been transmitted from the radio control transmitter. This is done by a process of subtraction. The difference between the two signals is passed to a controlling mechanism which uses a pre-selected strategy to make any correction required. The net result is that the servo – the corrective mechanism – applies a command to the hydroplanes based on the difference signal, and the actual value – the submarine's depth – alters. This type of system eliminates both the weaknesses outlined above.

Several different methods of producing the control signal from the difference between the actual and nominal values have been tried and found to work. The simplest is the "proportional regulator" (abbreviated to P regulator). In this case the command signal is the measured discrepancy multiplied by a fixed magnification factor. In this way the hydroplane movements are proportional to the deviation in depth. The more the boat deviates from the nominal depth, the larger the corrective command which is passed to the appropriate servo.

Unfortunately all regulatory circuits have the unpleasant habit of producing oscillation. If the regulator is incorrectly set the actual value goes up and down (oscillates) around the nominal value. A submarine fitted with a depth regulator of this type looks like a dolphin when submerged, constantly rising and falling around its nominal depth, breaking the water's surface at regular intervals if the nominal depth is shallow. The same effect occurs with an inexperienced operator using manual control. In terms of regulatory technology this represents a badly designed mechanism.

Practice makes perfect for the manual operator, and perfection in an automatic depth regulator just requires the correct settings. The oscillations will disappear if the regulatory amplification is kept at a low enough level, which means reducing the corrective hydroplane movements below a critical value for a given deviation from the nominal depth. This corresponds to a skilled submarine operator exercising good judgement in his use of the hydroplanes – just enough movement for just long enough. Too much corrective movement and the boat shoots past its target depth, and then has to be sent in the opposite direction to correct the new error. The whole thing ends up as a continuous oscillation, as already mentioned. On the other hand, if the amplification is at too low a level the hydroplanes will not move sufficiently, and the regulator will have no real effect.

Now that we know the typical problem, it is relatively easy to develop a procedure which will set the depth regulator correctly. We start with high regulator amplification (large hydroplane movements) and carry out a series of trial runs. Oscillations are bound to occur. We now reduce the amplification by regular increments – by altering the value of a resistor in the depth regulator – or by re-connecting the pushrod of a mechanical regulator to a different hole in the actuating lever. At some stage the continuous oscillations will just cease. The final level of amplification should be set to half of this value.

In many cases all that is required is regulation of the

submarine's attitude – i.e. its angle relative to the horizontal – rather than its actual depth. When the transmitter stick is at centre, the regulator is designed to ensure that the boat is running exactly horizontal and therefore at a constant depth. This method of pure attitude control compensates for the lack of weight stability when the model is at high speed, and thereby simplifies the task of the human "depth controller" standing on the bank.

A little thought shows that such a system will also simplify the task of the on-board electronic depth regulator, and it looks as if a combination of both systems might be a good idea. We then have two regulatory circuits which influence each other; the external depth regulator circuit (controlled from the transmitter) uses the internal attitude control circuit as its actuation system. This comprehensive form of regulation gives significantly better results, i.e. the accuracy with which the boat follows the commands from the transmitter is clearly greater with this process than with the use of a pressure sensor alone. In fact this is often the only reliable way of eliminating oscillation caused by the regulatory system.

With some models even this is not enough – particularly in the case of high-speed submarines with an inefficient hydroplane arrangement. This problem can be overcome by using a different control strategy, i.e. designing a regulator with different characteristics. Consider an efficient land-based regulator again (an experienced RC operator). He detects at an early stage when the boat is starting to sink (or rise), and he applies a corrective stick movement in good time. Similar tactics can be employed electronically, and such a system is called a "proportional differential regulator", abbreviated to PD regulator. With this system the rate of depth change is detected as well as the magnitude of the depth change, both deviations resulting in appropriate hydroplane deflections. In use this type of regulator appears to "think one step ahead".

The time span over which this correction action occurs has to be adjusted to match the inertia of the boat in question, otherwise it will not work properly. Fortunately this can be calculated from the duration, or period, of the oscillation, which can simply be measured during one of the trial runs mentioned above.

The regulator can only be matched perfectly to the characteristics of a particular submarine running at a particular speed. If the boat is run at a different speed, the set values will no longer apply and the depth control system will cease to work properly. If you are unwilling to take the highly complex route of handing over the task of depth control to a micro-processor, for which the correct regulator parameters for every speed and every hydroplane setting and every other influence have been stored, you have to accept a compromise. In practice an adequate solution is to set up the regulator to cope with the most difficult mode of operation – maximum speed. The system is then inevitably less accurate when the sub is at low speed, but even so the boat will not oscillate and the other typical problems will not arise.

When a submarine is running in reverse the effect of the hydroplanes is also reversed, so we have to accept that an attitude controller also works "the wrong way round" under those circumstances: when the boat's attitude is upset, instead of reducing the angle of pitch the regulator will increase it. A sensible solution to this problem is to switch back to manual operation, without any automatic control, for reverse running. The submarine then has no automatic stabilisation, but neither does it have active de-stabilisation, as would occur if the attitude regulator were left switched on. In any case you will need to switch off the regulator for certain extreme manoeuvres such as crash dives and loops, otherwise the system would limit the pitch angle of the vessel to about 5-10°.

I have described these regulatory circuits in abstract form, and there are several different methods of implementing them. Naturally, the neatest and most compact

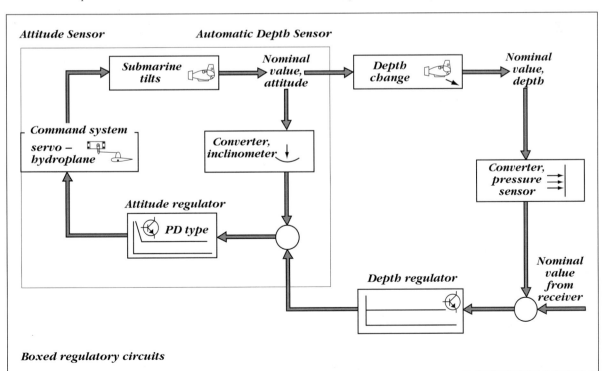

solution is to use electronic circuitry, which can be built both in digital – i.e. micro-processor controlled – or analogue form. The alternatives are mechanical systems and pneumatic systems.

Mechanical regulators

The earliest depth regulators were the mechanical types used in Whitehead torpedoes in the last century. As late as the 1960's modern submarines were still fitted with mechanical systems, although they were only used for cruising by then.

The design of these devices is extremely simple: the sensor, pendulum and pressure membrane are built large enough to control the hydroplanes directly. The planes are designed to be free-moving and balanced [what is called mass balancing in aircraft], i.e. the pivot axis is located around the 25% point of the chord measured from the leading edge. Waterproof gaskets would reduce the freedom of movement, so the pendulum and pressure sensor are usually set up in a free flooding compartment. If two pairs of hydroplanes are fitted, two sensors are installed, working independently of each other to control their own pair of planes. Where that is not possible some form of coupling – for example a lever – can be used to inter-connect the two movements.

Unfortunately the force which such a pendulum can exert on the hydroplanes is quite small, with the result that the planes tend to affect the pendulum (i.e. movement in the opposite direction), and this is an inherent drawback of the system.

The natural frequency of the pendulum is relatively slow, and if the pendulum is very long it may be so slow that it is incapable of providing any effective control.

On the other hand the pendulum is extremely heavy (1-2kg) and has the side-effect of reducing the boat's metacentric height, as the point on which its force acts is its pivot bearing, and not its centre of gravity. The overall result is that a mechanical regulator can only provide an improvement in longitudinal stability (and thus depth control) if a reduction in weight stability is acceptable. The improvement in dynamic stability is only slight, and

the balance between these factors has to be adjusted very accurately. This usually involves a protracted testing program.

For this reason some form of force amplifier needs to be installed between pendulum and control surface. Pneumatic and electrical follower systems immediately come to mind. Standard modelling servos also represent a form of follower system, so what could be more obvious than to use the hydroplane servo itself as a force amplifier. In this case the sensors would only influence the servo's control system.

Inclinometer

This is the technical term for a device which measures an angle relative to the horizontal and converts it into another form. Without exception inclinometers consist of a pendulum and a mechanism which converts the deflection angle into an electrical value.

The simplest design is just a weight on a lever, attached to the shaft of a potentiometer. However, pot shafts are extremely stiff, so the pendulum would have to be very large to overcome this. A 200g weight on a 130mm long lever, fixed to a normal pot with a 6mm shaft, exhibits a mean deviation of about one degree. If the pot spindle is rotated slowly the deviation can amount to 2.5 degrees. Both the lever length and the inaccuracy are excessive for an attitude regulation system.

The pendulum's oscillation period would be 0.73 seconds, and that is so slow that it approaches the oscillation period of the submarine when it is in motion. This in itself would tend to make the regulatory circuit unstable. To avoid problems in this area it is advisable to limit the oscillation period to no more than one tenth of the oscillation period of the submarine. With a small high-speed boat this value may be as low as one second (measured on a 1:30 scale "V80"), but is usually in the 5 seconds range with large models. The inclinometer pendulum should carry out one oscillation in less than 0.1-0.5 seconds.

The mathematician's theoretical pendulum has all its mass concentrated at one point, and in this case the

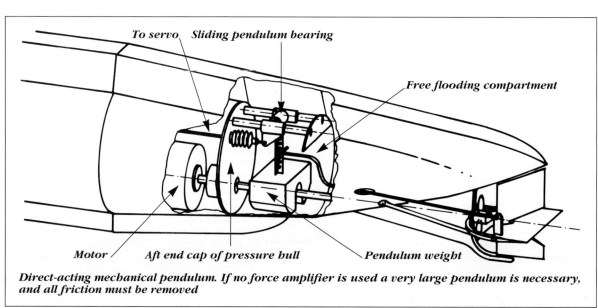

Direct-acting mechanical pendulum. If no force amplifier is used a very large pendulum is necessary, and all friction must be removed

An early version of a mechanical attitude regulator (several years old)

period varies only according to the length of the pendulum. The formula is this:

$$T = 2\pi\sqrt{\frac{1}{g}}$$

or in other words:

$$1 = \left(\frac{T}{2\pi}\right)^2 g$$

where

l: Length of pendulum in m
g: Acceleration due to gravity 9.81m/s²
T: Period in seconds

The weight of a real pendulum has a certain size, of course, so the formula is not very accurate. Nevertheless it provides quite useful results for our purpose.

The maximum range of pendulums is therefore 2.4 to 62mm in length, depending on the size of the boat. You can expect an oscillation period of more than 2 seconds with model submarines of medium size, and this calls for a pendulum length of no more than 10mm. In practice this is adequate in 99% of models. However, you still need to carry out trial runs to establish the boat's behaviour.

It is now clear that making a usable inclinometer requires skills usually associated with a watchmaker. But

don't be put off: model makers often have to construct small mechanical devices of similar size, so the problem does not appear to be insoluble.

While we are on the subject of timepieces: an extremely good pendulum can be made from the balance component of a mechanical alarm clock by sawing off the wheel, leaving only one spoke. The point bearing is retained and gives us the very low friction which we require. Of course, the sensor section must also be low in friction. One arrangement which has proved effective is a pair of photo-transistors combined with an LED. The photo-transistors are wired as voltage dividers and half the width of each is covered by a paddle at the point of the pendulum, designed in the form of a light shade. If the pendulum moves, more of the paddle covers one transistor than the other, and the output voltage alters accordingly.

Eliminating friction in this way unfortunately introduces a new problem: if the pendulum should encounter a shock force it will continue swinging long afterwards (more than 20 oscillations). During this period the measured values will be completely unstable. Friction must be built back into the system, but in a controlled way so that the oscillations decay rapidly. We have to be careful to keep this damping effect within limits, otherwise the pendulum will be very slow to creep to its new position. The optimum level of damping is easy to define: the output signal should return to rest after a single oscillation.

Unfortunately we cannot just tighten up the bearing, as friction is much higher when the moving body is

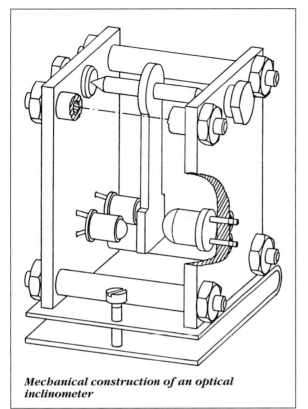

Mechanical construction of an optical inclinometer

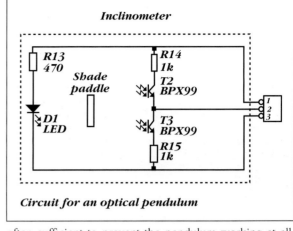

Circuit for an optical pendulum

static or at very low speed than when it is moving faster. The result is that the pendulum moves in jerks and exhibits hysteresis, i.e. at the bottom of the range of movement (of the housing) there is a point below which the pendulum fails to move at all. A better solution is to introduce friction by means of a viscous fluid. A generous application of thick grease at the point bearing is often sufficient to prevent the pendulum working at all. However, good long-term results are obtained by encapsulating the pendulum and immersing it in oil.

The next stage of development is to eliminate the mechanical pendulum altogether, and use the fluid itself as a pendulum. If we can manage that, there are no moving parts left and the watchmaker can be sent home to bed. The attitude of the liquid can be sensed by exploiting its own conductivity using three electrodes, again wired as a voltage divider. One little problem is that the electrodes and the oil will be electrolytically decomposed if a DC current is applied to them, so we have to feed the system an alternating current (AC). This is not difficult, but it does render the sensing circuit that much more complicated.

One version which has worked out well is based on a measurement chamber 16mm in diameter and 2mm thick, giving an oscillation period of 0.195 seconds. The electrodes are etched from standard circuit board material. They are gold-plated to extend their useful life, but this not absolutely essential. The cover can be machined from plastic (don't use PMMA – perspex) or cast in resin, and attached using cyano-acrylate adhesive. The fluid consists of 90% alcohol (10% water to improve conductivity), and the chamber should be exactly half-filled using an insulin syringe. The filler hole can be sealed with a screw and teflon tape.

The sensor circuit consists of three components. An NE 555 chip produces an alternating current of about 1.5kHz. Harmonics are filtered out by means of de-coupling capacitors, and the current is then fed to the measurement chamber. At this frequency the conductivity of the fluid is at its maximum. The

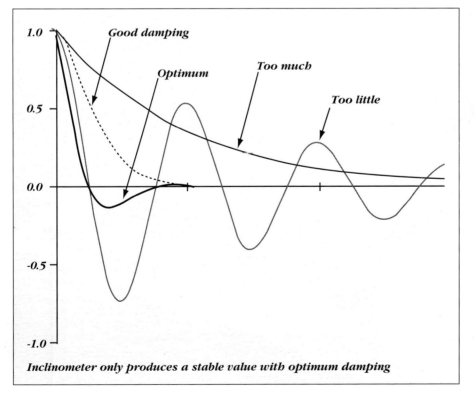

Inclinometer only produces a stable value with optimum damping

output signal is an alternating voltage of varying amplitude which in turn is processed by a voltage doubling rectifier. Residual carrier frequency signals are filtered out, leaving the signal we want, but at a very low level. It is now brought up to a usable level by means of an op-amp (operational amplifier). At this point a zero point trimmer is incorporated in the form of a potentiometer. If you are better at earning money than constructing electronic circuits there are ready-made inclinometers available commercially, and these work on the same principle. I happen to think that laying out £20-£30 for such a little thing is, shall we say, unsporting (oh come on – it's only a hobby!), but if you disagree you will find a list of companies in the appendix who will be pleased to help you.

It should be obvious that the inclinometer has to be screwed firmly to the boat and must be orientated exactly in the fore-and-aft direction. If your inclinometer lacks any electronic facility to adjust the horizontal, you can make a mechanical version in the form of an adjustable tilting base. Setting this value accurately is crucial to the precision of the attitude regulation system. If you find that your inclinometer drifts out of adjustment over time, you will have to correct the setting at regular intervals.

Pressure sensors

One design principle has also become dominant with this type of sensor. It consists of a membrane or a curved tube which is distorted by pressure and thereby moves an electrical transducer. This again can be a potentiometer – with all its inherent disadvantages – or an optical sensor based on photo-transistors. Expansion measurement strips can also be used.

If you want to make your own pressure sensor an ordinary manometer is a good starting point. Inside the

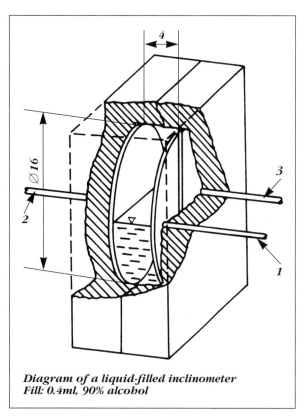

Diagram of a liquid-filled inclinometer
Fill: 0.4ml, 90% alcohol

unit you will find a sickle-shaped arc of thin-walled flattened tube. Internal pressure tends to straighten out the curve. This movement is usually transmitted to the manometer needle via gears, but it can be measured optically using the arrangement already described for the inclinometer.

Inclinometer construction using etched electrodes

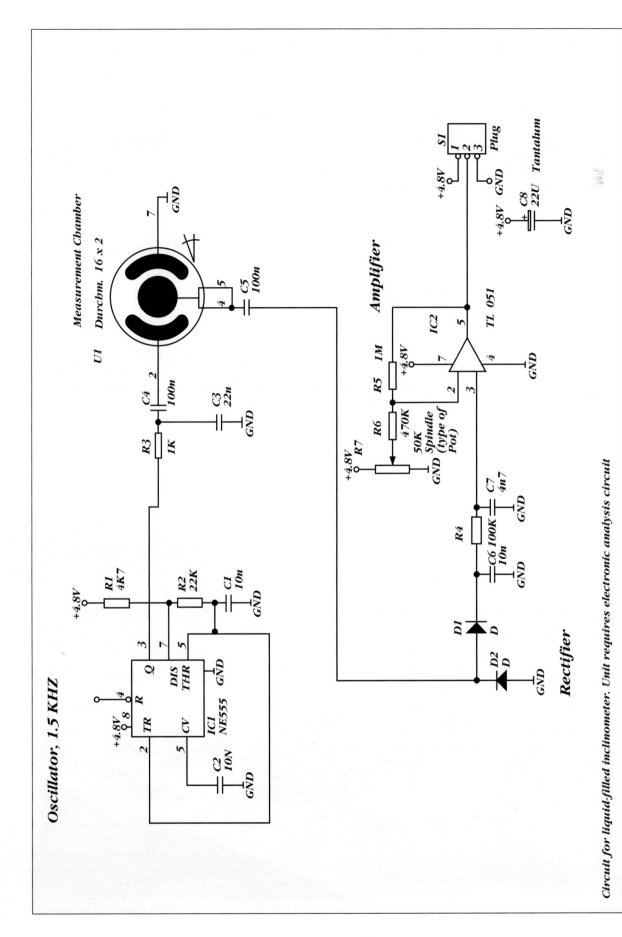

Circuit for liquid-filled inclinometer. Unit requires electronic analysis circuit

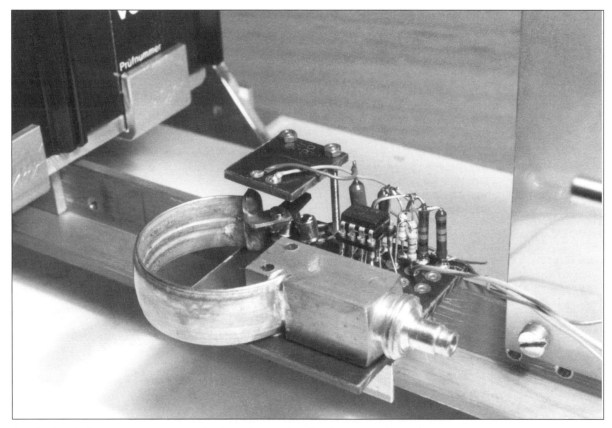

An electronic pressure sensor can be based on a standard manometer

The unit's sensitivity should be adjusted to cope with a range of pressures from 0 to 0.2 bar (corresponding to 2 mWS). A home-made pressure sensor of this type is not that accurate and by no means linear, but that is not an important drawback for our purpose. However, the influence of ambient pressure on the measured value can cause problems. All the pressure sensor can do is measure the difference between water pressure and the boat's internal pressure, but this means that any change in internal pressure, due to a variation in temperature or a movement of the diving cell piston, has the same effect on the sensor as a change in depth.

The alternative is to use a pressure sensor based on an integrated circuit (IC, or chip). These are much smaller in size, much more accurate and above all independent of ambient pressure. They consist of a metal case 12mm in diameter housing a silicon chip. The chip serves as pressure membrane and also contains the four

A KPY 10 pressure sensor cut open to show the unprotected chip, which would be destroyed by water

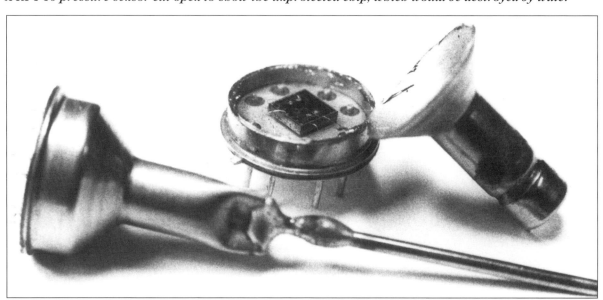

highly sensitive expansion measurement strips. In some versions the processing circuit is also integrated into the same chip.

With the exception of special-purpose, special-price types these modules will only tolerate gaseous media, and certainly not corrosive liquids. They must therefore be protected from water by enclosing them in a suitable pressure medium converter. Experiments with a rubber membrane about 5cm² in area located immediately adjacent to the pressure sensor, using air as the transfer medium, have been successful in some cases. Silicone oil works well as the transfer medium, using a 30mm length of 0.5mm capillary tube (smallest size of heat-shrink sleeving after heating) to separate the device from the water.

It is essential not to introduce air bubbles when filling the device with oil, and this is done by sealing the system then using a syringe to apply vacuum and pressure alternately. The tube is better glued in place for this purpose can also be used to form the connection between the sensor and the hull opening. The output signal from these sensors is a voltage difference of only a few mV, and this must therefore be amplified by a suitable circuit.

The position of the hull opening has an important influence on the pressure which registers when the boat is running. If it is located at the bow, pressure builds up due to the vessel's speed through the water. At the bow this can amount to 9.6mbar at 5km/hr. The depth regulator thinks that the boat is 9.6cm too deep and forces it to climb by the same amount. If the sensor opening is at the stern the opposite effect occurs. If it is on one side of the hull any turn will also cause a difference in pressure which will confuse the depth regulator. If you consider all these unwanted effects to be unacceptable, the only position left is midships in the keel.

Direct-connected inclinometers

The simplest method of passing the inclinometer's signal to the servo is a direct connection to the servo's feedback pot. In this case it is better to use an inclinometer without any electronics and save yourself some money – i.e. make one based on an optical sensor. The two photo-transistors are connected in parallel to the pot, so the servo electronics process an "actual" value which is different from the one which is really present. The electronic circuit corrects this by moving the pot and thereby the hydroplanes by a corresponding amount. In practical terms the information from the pot is subtracted from the value received from the inclinometer, and this corresponds to the actual-nominal comparison of the regulatory circuit which we have previously discussed in theoretical terms.

This idea has already been tested with servos which see a pure DC voltage of about 2.5V at the feedback potentiometer. This is the case with servo electronics based on the NE 544 chip. The sensitivity of the inclinometer can be set by adjusting the brightness of the LED (using R1) or via a resistor (R2). This simple design cannot be used to produce the regulatory characteristics of a proportional differential (PD) regulator.

Unfortunately this modification invariably increases the maximum travel of the servo. If the servo or hydroplanes are fitted with mechanical end-stops, then the motor may be stalled. In practice this often occurs and the motor then suffers damage.

A simple attitude regulator

Many modellers will not be happy about modifying servos, and an alternative is to pass the output voltage from the inclinometer to an additional electronic circuit which is wired between receiver and servo. The circuit incorporates a servo travel limit which can be thought of as an "electronic end-stop". This prevents the servo being damaged by running against its mechanical stops.

The circuit presented here is not particularly refined, but it is simple to build and very reliable in operation. A relay can be incorporated in the inclinometer's signal wire so that you can switch off the regulator, i.e. revert to manual control, at any time.

The DC voltage from the sensor is converted into a pulsed signal using a universal timer of the NE 555 or ½ NE 556 type. The first module works as a power-off delay and extends the signal coming from the receiver by an amount which varies according to the voltage at the control input. This stage is the true regulator in which the actual and nominal values are added together. Next comes a power-on delay which shortens the signal back to a constant level, so that its length is in the range 1.5 +/- 0.5ms, which the servo can process. Another sensor such as a pressure sensor can be connected to the input of this stage (IC 1, pin 11) if required.

The third and fourth timers are started at the beginning of this temporary output signal, and supply comparison signals which are of

Syringe used to fill pressure sensor with silicone oil without introducing air bubbles.

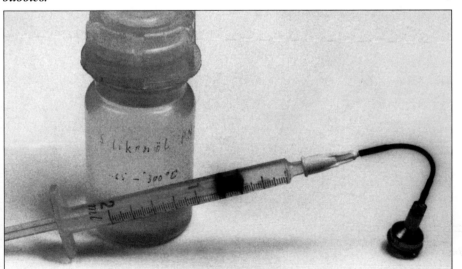

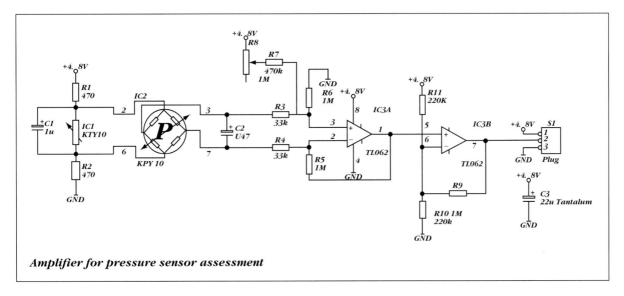

Amplifier for pressure sensor assessment

maximum (2ms) and minimum (1ms) duration. The NOR gates are wired in such a way that the output signal is only passed through if it lies within this range. If not, then the comparison signal is passed through instead.

Once the circuit has been constructed you have to adjust the three trim pots and the horizontal position of the attitude sensor. This is the procedure: install and connect the whole radio control system, but leave the hydroplane linkages and the wires to the inclinometer unconnected for the moment. All the pots should be at centre. Set the transmitter stick to centre and adjust the "zero" pot until the servo is at centre. The "min" and "max" pots can now be adjusted until the servo travel is just short of its mechanical end-stops at full stick movement in both directions. At this point it should be possible to control the servo from the transmitter as if the regulator were not there at all. Now connect the inclinometer and the hydroplanes and adjust the inclinometer base to the point where the hydroplanes are level when the boat is horizontal (check with a spirit level).

Tilt the boat, and the hydroplanes should visibly move in the opposite direction. If the hydroplanes respond, but in the wrong direction, the inclinometer is the wrong way round.

Depth regulator

In addition to the attitude regulator sub-assemblies this circuit includes the control electronics for the liquid inclinometer, the silicon pressure sensor, the PD regulator and the manual transfer circuit. The use of more refined circuit technology has nevertheless made it possible to keep the number of ICs the same. Part of the circuit takes the form of an analogue computer with op-amps, while the rest processes pulsed signals.

The main drive battery is the system's power supply, and should provide at least 6 Volts. The integral voltage regulator then provides a smooth and stable 5 Volt supply to the circuit. Of course, you could power it directly from the receiver battery if you can accept the

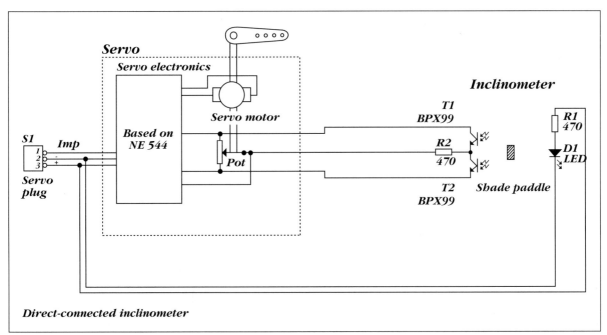

Direct-connected inclinometer

The simplest solution is a direct connection between the inclinometer and the hydroplane servo

rectangular pulse is again present at the output of OP, and this signal controls the servo.

The two monoflops contained in IC2 produce the comparison pulses for maximum and minimum. "Max" is triggered by the input signal and abruptly cuts off the square pulse via D5 and R3. "Min" is started by the output pulse and holds the output at "1" via D6 and R7.

The control circuit for the liquid inclinometer is similar to that already presented, although in this case the multi-vibrator consists of analogue switches. The PD regulator is connected directly to the rectifier. Its delay time is determined by C13. The signal is passed to the adder via

potentially lower reliability. In this case you don't need the voltage regulator, and it can be bridged by a length of wire.

The "pulse width modulator" sub-assembly works in exactly the same way as the attitude regulator already described. The pulse from the receiver is extended or shortened according to the control voltage, but stays within the range 1 to 2ms. After the buffer stage, which includes the analogue switch IC3D, the pulse controls the integrator by means of IC1A. This produces a triangular form of voltage which is converted to square form as it passes through D1 and D2. At this stage the voltage is +/- 1.6V relative to virtual earth. This square-form voltage is now compared with the control voltage at IC1B. A

IC1C together with the very small output voltage from the pressure sensor and a zero point correction. The amplification of the regulatory circuit is determined by the resistor R25. The two LEDs limit the output voltage to +/- 1.4V, to ensure that the voltage deviation of the square generator is not exceeded. Incidentally, the LEDs glow visibly.

If the analogue switch IC3A is opened, the regulator reverts to manual operation. The pressure sensor then has no effect and the amplification of the attitude regulator is greatly reduced. This results in a small stabilising effect which can be over-ridden from the transmitter at any time.

A small supplementary circuit including T1 allows the analogue switch to be controlled by a proportional channel. The switching point is set by adjusting the pot R31. If a proportional channel is used the input can be left open, and the depth regulator is then active. If it is connected to a positive voltage of more than 2V (for example via a switched channel), then the regulator switches to manual operation.

Construction should not present problems to anyone with experience in using a soldering iron and working on small circuit boards. Only one bridge has to be fitted on the underside, and

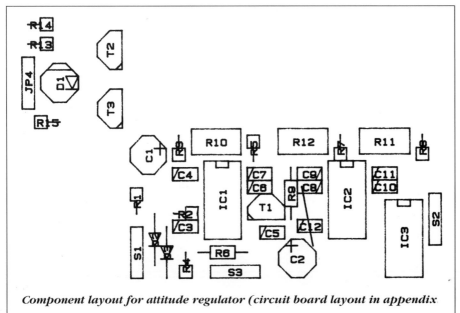

Component layout for attitude regulator (circuit board layout in appendix

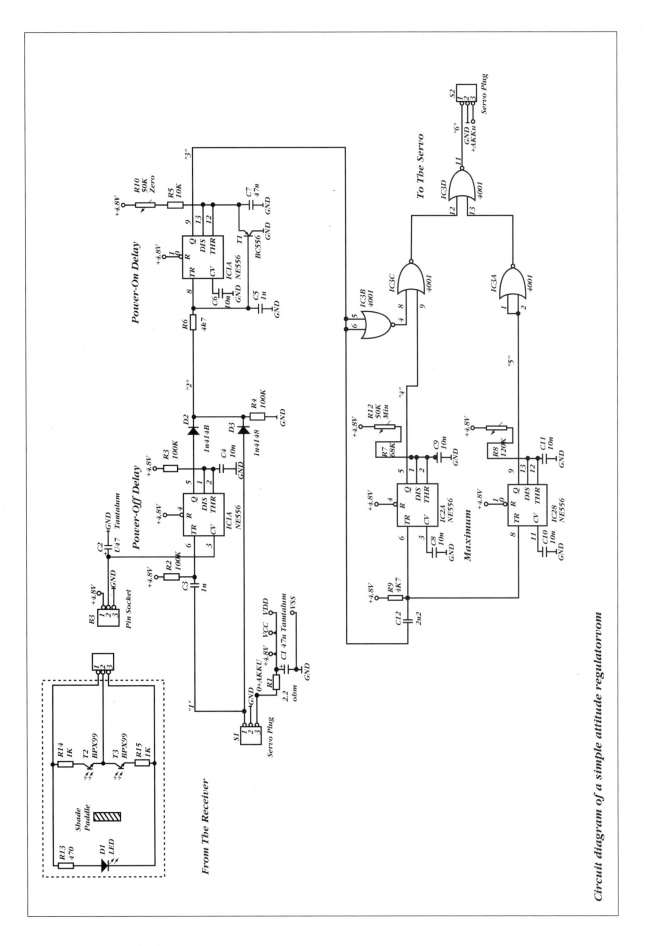

Circuit diagram of a simple attitude regulatorvom

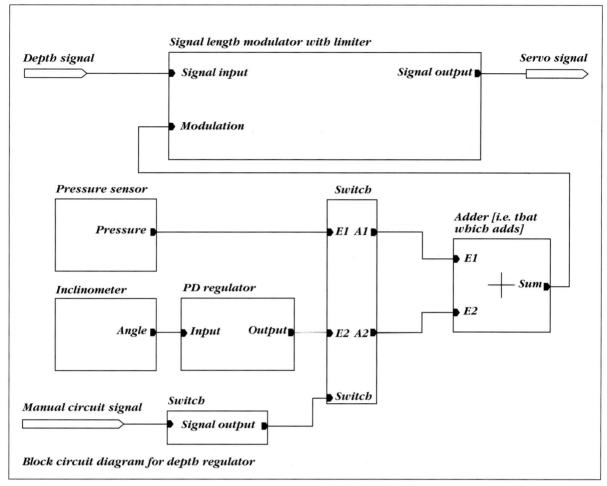

Signal length modulator with limiter

Depth signal → Signal input   Signal output → Servo signal

Modulation

Pressure sensor — Pressure → E1 A1

Switch

Adder [i.e. that which adds] — E1, E2, Sum

Inclinometer — Angle → PD regulator Input — Output → E2 A2

Manual circuit signal → Switch Signal output → Switch

Block circuit diagram for depth regulator

this should be of lacquered copper wire. All the ICs, the inclinometer and the tuneable components R25, R28 and C13 are socketed. Prepare the pressure sensor and inclinometer as already described. All inputs and outputs are taken to a five-pin terminal block, so that the circuit board can easily be removed from the submarine. Naturally the circuit board must be orientated in the correct direction and must be mounted securely. If space is at a premium it can also be installed in any orientation provided that the inclinometer is mounted in the correct position and connected by a cable.

A modicum of care is called for when adjusting the five pots. With the system connected to a receiver and servo the first step is to determine the switching point threshold for manual transfer by adjusting R31. When the switching point is reached the servo should move normally. Select manual operation (if necessary connect the manual circuit's input to 5V) and set the servo to centre by adjusting R20 "horizontal". The electronic stops are set using R16 "max" and R17 "min", and you should take care that the servo stops just short of its end-stops at full movement of the transmitter stick. Now switch to regulator operation and set the hydroplanes to "slightly down" by adjusting R21 "depth". The submarine should then keep to a depth of about 20 to 50cm when the stick is at centre. You can correct this value if necessary during initial trial runs.

However, the most difficult phase is yet to come: establishing the optimum regulatory parameters. This is done by adjusting parts R25 and C13 which determine

those aspects of the system. The easiest method is to observe the submarine's tendency to oscillate when running. The first step is to omit the capacitor C13, and switch the unit to manual operation, so that you are using the system purely as a proportional attitude regulator. Now vary the resistor R28, starting with a large value, until the model just oscillates. This does actually involve lifting the submarine out of the water and opening it a dozen times, as the resistor has to be replaced each time. It is a good idea to start by making coarse changes (for example 1MOhm, 100kOhm, 10kOhm), and then to use ever finer increments as you approach the optimum value. You could use a pot to circumvent this procedure, but this would not necessarily provide the necessary accuracy over the wide variation range required.

Once you find the value at which oscillations just occur, you should measure the oscillation period using a stopwatch.

The final values are then:

R25: $R_{test} \times 2$
R28:   R25 $\times$ 5

C13 (in μF): $\dfrac{Period}{6.28}$

You may find that the trial procedure fails to produce usable values, and in this case you should suspect the model submarine itself.

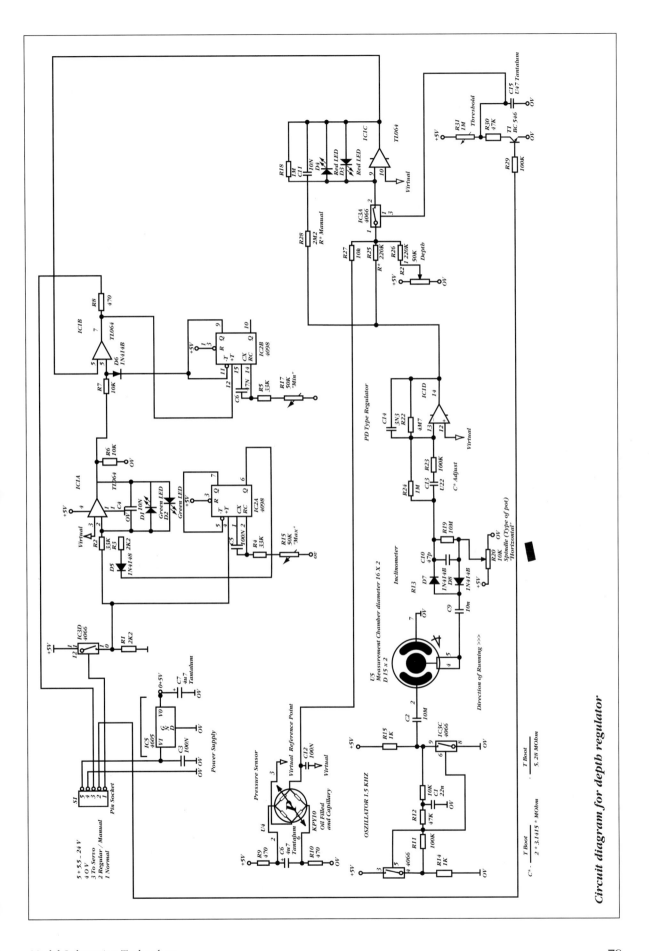

Circuit diagram for depth regulator

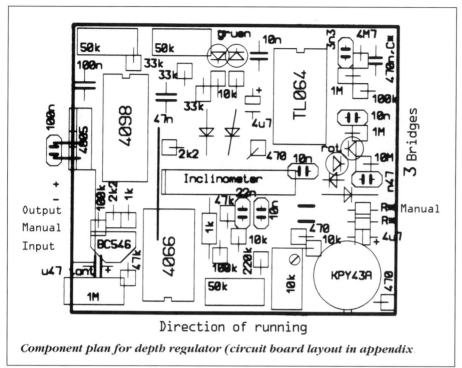

Component plan for depth regulator (circuit board layout in appendix.

correct it by re-positioning the ballast.

Further possibilities

The area of automatic regulation offers plenty of scope for technical experimentation – in model submarines more than any other type of model. Indeed, some experts have made this their speciality, and you can usually recognise their boats by their very spartan external appearance; they are simply more interested in what's going on inside.

The depth regulator usually controls the model's hydroplanes, but it can also act upon the diving cell so that you can achieve a stable

If the metacentric height is great, the boat is probably impossible to control in any case. The fault then lies not in the regulator, but in the submarine, and you should "hover" (constant depth) when the boat is stationary at any depth. The depth regulator presented here can be used for this purpose if appropriately modified. In this

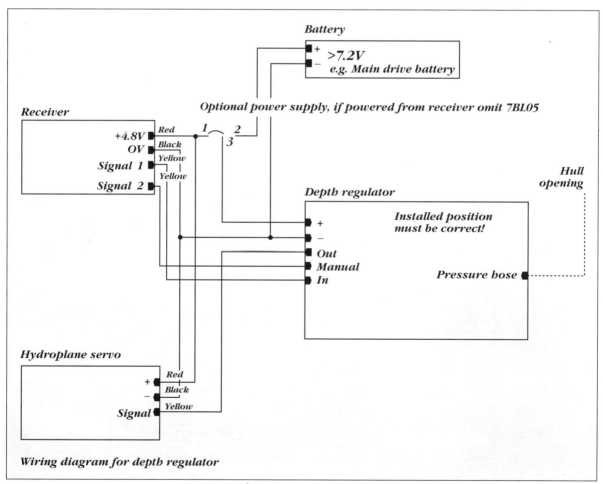

Wiring diagram for depth regulator

case the inclinometer and its associated circuitry are omitted, the PD regulator is looped into the signal path of the pressure sensor and the delay time matched to the slower behaviour of the submarine during static diving operations. Naturally, the diving cell must be fitted with a proportional control system. This type of automatic mechanism has been installed in full-size submarines such as the type XXI U-boat, and therefore counts as a scale feature.

It may also make sense to fit a roll regulator if your submarine has a powerful motor and a single screw. Such a system reduces the metacentric height in order to improve the boat's manoeuvring capability, without propeller torque causing too great an angle of heel. In this variant the inclinometer is installed laterally, together with special lateral control surfaces [equivalent of ailerons] for it to control. The regulatory circuit can be the attitude regulator already presented here, or alternatively the depth regulator circuit with the pressure sensor replaced by two resistors.

The roll planes can take the form of a second pair of hydroplanes whose panels are designed to rotate in opposite directions. An alternative is to use the existing

The completed depth regulator circuit board is 55 x 65mm in size

hydroplanes but link each to a separate servo and utilise a transmitter mixer to superimpose the functions.

A particularly wayward modelling colleague of mine owns a model submarine whose rudder is also regulated, this time by a compass. Thus his boat maintains a perfect course even when it is submerged in murky water, and completely out of the operator's control.

As can be seen from the block circuit diagram the whole business of regulation can easily acquire the

Helmut Huhn is able to control all three boats simultaneously, as they are largely automatic in operation

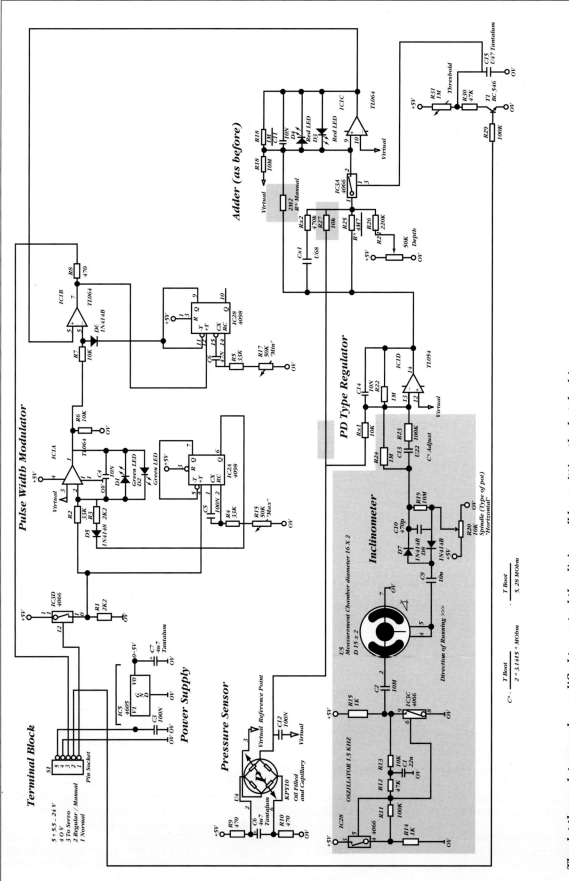

The depth regulator can be modified to control the diving cell by omitting the hatched-in areas

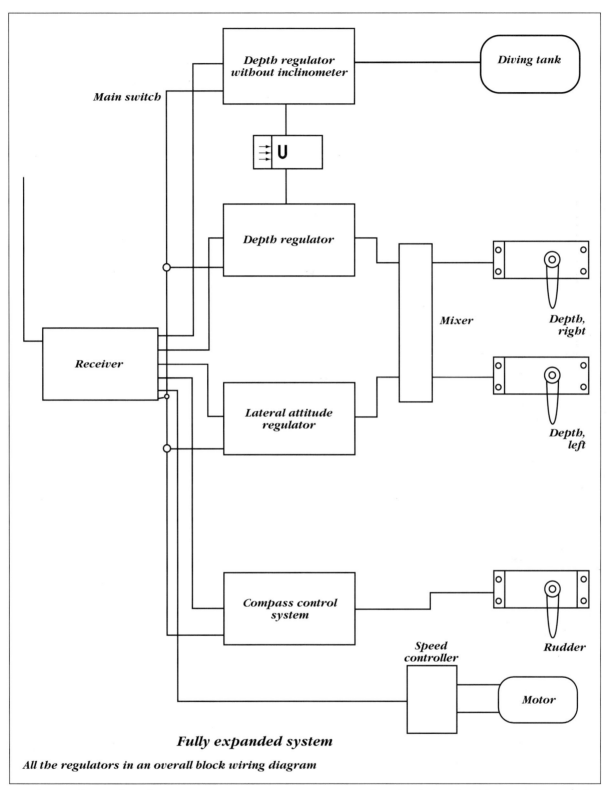

**Depth regulator
without inclinometer**

Diving tank

Main switch

U

Depth regulator

Mixer

**Depth,
right**

Receiver

**Lateral attitude
regulator**

**Depth,
left**

**Compass control
system**

Rudder

**Speed
controller**

Motor

Fully expanded system

All the regulators in an overall block wiring diagram

complexity of a moderately extensive stereo system. The circuit boards required for a comprehensive system can quickly soak up all the space available in a small boat, not to mention the endless tangles of wire. However, all the effort is justified by the model's performance, and there is just no other way of obtaining it.

A long overdue development is a sensible micro-processor based solution for this extremely complex task. It seems that modellers don't often have a natural instinct for computers, and computer freaks don't always seem to be attracted to model submarines.

Where separate specialist areas meet but fail to overlap, technical advance is often much slower than the sensational announcements about the latest generation of super-computers would sometimes have us believe.

Chapter 10

Safety

Radio contact

Electro-magnetic waves are absorbed by water, since the medium is conductive and practically shorts them out. This characteristic is almost the opposite of air, in which the waves can propagate virtually unhindered. Nevertheless, even in water radio waves are able to penetrate to a certain depth, although that depth varies according to the conductivity of the water and the frequency of the radio waves.

The radio control frequencies of 27 and 40MHz which are in most common use lie in the short wave region, with wave lengths of 11 and 7.5m. Over this distance the electrical resistance of fresh water is very high, with the result that reception quality is good and continues unabated to a depth of about 10m. If the water is more conductive, radio reception collapses earlier. In a chlorinated swimming pool radio contact fails at a depth of about 3.5m, and in sea water at just 5cm.

The permanently submerged atomic submarines maintain radio contact on very long wave at around 10kHz at which frequency the wave length is around 30km. These waves can penetrate a great distance even in seawater. The drawback is very low transmission speed – only morse code is possible – and very long (drag) aerials are required – several kilometres in length.

Precisely the opposite situation arises with radio control systems on the 433MHz band. Their wave length is only 70cm and they are much more sensitive to water conductivity than 40MHz systems.

However, these systems have very sophisticated receivers, are extremely good at rejecting interference, and are highly sensitive. These advantages cancel out the drawback, and the systems are certainly suitable for use in model submarines.

One particular problem for model submarines is the arrangement of the receiver aerial. Submarines do not have a large superstructure, far less a tall mast along which to run a vertical 1m long whip aerial. The most favourable solution is to exploit the forestay which is present on many submarines, and which also serves as aerial on the full-size vessel. It makes no difference whether the aerial is isolated from the water or not, as the radio waves are in constant contact with the water in any case. If there are no wires tensioned above deck the only alternative is to deploy the aerial inside the hull. If you take this route, the most important rule is that you keep the aerial as far away as possible from all metal parts in general, and power conductors in particular. To obtain reliable results with your radio system it is essential to consider the radio installation in your model at the design stage, so that you can work out how best to keep the parts carrying heavy currents as far distant as possible from the aerial. Even metal frames and hatch covers can prevent the system working properly.

The inefficiency of the aerial arrangement in model submarines means that all electric motors must be very effectively suppressed – even more carefully than with a surface-running model boat. A good starting point is to select high-quality motors with multi-part commutators. Twelve hours' running-in under no-load conditions from a mains-powered D.C. power supply will bed in the carbon brushes well, and this reduces the brush sparking which usually causes so much interference.

Safety measures

Every model boat enthusiast who has ever placed his model in its element is bound to consider now and then that one day he may go home with only his transmitter under his arm. The likelihood of losing a model is not high, but every now and then salvage operations have to be carried out, and swimming trunks or even diving apparatus are the order of the day. The same applies to model submarines.

It is highly improbable that a surface vessel would ever sink just because its power system and/or control system failed. And this is where the crucial difference lies: if you suffer a system failure with your submarine and it happens to be trimmed just heavier than water, it will inexorably sink to the bottom. The model will suffer no damage from this – it's completely watertight, of course – but that won't stop the owner worrying, or getting a little damp in salvaging his submarine.

Some failures can be avoided if you incorporate sensible safety systems in the model, but you cannot reasonably hope to cover all possibilities; there will always be some stupid coincidence which you have not considered. It is unfortunately the case that any safety measures you take add extra complication to the boat's construction and make it more difficult to check and maintain. In this sense safety measures can make a model more susceptible to accidents rather than less so. Instead of installing an unreliable system and then fitting an unpredictable safety measure to guard against its failure, it makes much more sense to build the thing sensibly in the first place, and incorporate "built-in" reliability. I have come across several boats which are virtually never lowered into the water because one or other of the safety circuits always seems to trip just before launch, and disables the boat automatically to prevent further damage.

A good principle to adopt if you want to produce a reliable system is to use as few components as possible and keep those components as simple as possible. This "simplify everything" principle runs counter to the

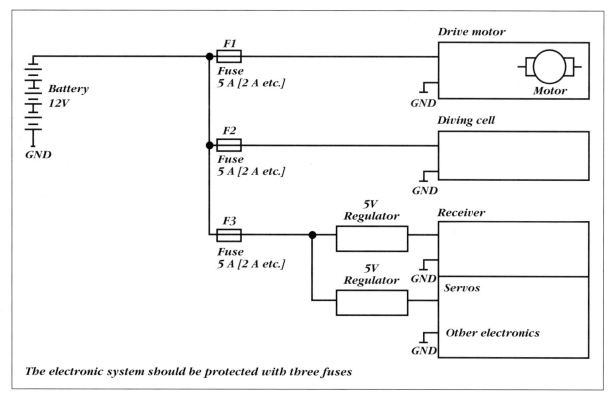

The electronic system should be protected with three fuses

instincts of many modellers, who often like to make a mechanism as complex as possible just for the fun of it. The same applies to the number of components, where many models could safely "lighten up".

This has particular relevance to batteries. At present the standard guideline seems to be: the more, the better. This philosophy results in unnecessary weight combined with reduced reliability. If you have six different batteries in your boat, you can almost guarantee that one of them is either flat or has outlived its useful life because of long-term non-use. The most reliable model submarine will be the one with only one battery; the likelihood of that one battery failing is only one sixth of the six-battery vessel just mentioned.

Batteries not only go flat, they are also capable of endangering the health of your model and its owner. The hazard is hydrogen, which is released by all kinds of batteries under certain circumstances, and which mixes with air to form an explosive mixture. In a surface vessel the hydrogen can simply drift away, but not in a hermetically sealed submarine. Fortunately for us, the main time when hydrogen is formed is during the charging process. For this reason it is an absolute rule that batteries must never be recharged with the submarine sealed, even though that is obviously the most elegant method. A number of nasty accidents have already occurred due to exploding hydrogen. The submarine must be left open during the charging process, and then kept open afterwards for a while for any gas to diffuse away before it may safely be sealed again.

Individual battery types exhibit widely differing characteristics in terms of gassing. "Wet" lead/acid batteries with loose acid produce most gas, and they do so during charging and discharging, but fortunately they are very seldom used in modelling. They are attitude-sensitive and tend to give off a constant minute flow of very finely atomised acid, so in every way they are unsuitable for

model submarines. They have a place in full-size submarines, but for that application they are fitted with sophisticated gas suction systems and in any case are set up in separate battery compartments. For modelling purposes the only types of battery used to any great extent are sealed lead-acid types and nickel-cadmium packs, both of which give off gas, but only when overcharged. In normal operation you can be confident about using them safely. However, it is impossible to exclude altogether the possibility of overcharging, so batteries should only ever be charged with the submarine opened up.

Testing for leaks

If a model submarine is to be reliable and have a long life, it is absolutely essential that it is completely watertight. Just a few drops of water penetrating the hull moisten the atmosphere to such an extent that condensation forms everywhere. Neither the electronics nor the steel parts will survive long if they have to live in a fog. If the boat is then left sealed at home for several weeks, failure of some system or other is almost inevitable.

Leaks often only occur after a long period of use or after a repair. Because of this it is essential that you carry out regular checks. A good method is to increase the air pressure inside the hull slightly with a few strokes of a bicycle pump. If the boat is in good shape the excess pressure should be maintained for several hours, and you should distinctly hear it escape when you open the valve. If you think you have a problem, submerge the boat in water and a stream of air bubbles will show up the location of any leak. Many modellers pump up their boats slightly every time they are about to place them in the water, as they then have a good check on the state of the seals at the start of the run. A standard bicycle valve and valve rubber can be used, as these valves do not open until a pressure of 2 bar is reached. That means that they will seal reliably against water pressure, but can still be filled using an air pump.

Electrical safety measures

In every model boat the electrical system should be protected as standard by ordinary fuses. If the batteries are short-circuited they can produce gigantic currents of several hundred amps – sufficient to make quite heavy cables glow. This invariably results in substantial damage to the model. The sensitive electronics should be protected separately by a fuse with a much lower rating.

If a cable fire should occur in a model submarine, the operator can neither smell nor see it; after all, it takes place in a sealed container. A sensible fuse arrangement is therefore a fundamental necessity. Even so, it makes sense to ensure that a fault which blows a single fuse cannot result in the loss of the model. A system of three fuses protecting the drive motor, diving cell and receiving system circuits respectively has proved effective. If the drive motor fuse blows, all the control surfaces and the diving cell will still work, and the submarine can even be brought back to the bank by a continuous dive/surface cycle "on the glide". If the receiving system fails, the diving cell failsafe system should trip, and cause the tank to empty completely. You will no longer be able to manoeuvre the boat, but at least it is on the surface. The most critical problem is failure of the diving cell, and if the submarine is already on the bottom, you have a salvage job on your hands. Otherwise the boat can still be kept on the surface using the motor and hydroplanes, and you can then start salvage operations.

Even if your model submarine is apparently working faultlessly, there are a number of completely unpredictable occurrences which may bring things to a halt. The measures described in the next section are intended to help you in such circumstances.

Transmitter failsafe

A failsafe circuit monitors the control signals which arrive at the submarine after transmission from the transmitter. If the proper signal fails to arrive, the failsafe automatically empties the diving tank; all the other control systems are held at neutral or idle. This usually occurs when the boat descends too far, and the radio waves can no longer penetrate to the model in that particular type of water. This is not really a case of interference but an aspect of normal operations – even if it is an undesirable aspect. Without an automatic rescue system the boat would sink to the bottom and be out of your control completely – and that would certainly count as an accident.

Automatic failsafe systems of this type are available under the deceptive name of "auto-pilot" (Conrad Electronic), so we don't need to provide a circuit diagram here. The servo circuit for diving cells already described in this book includes a failsafe function.

Battery monitor

No matter how many batteries are installed in your model, it is important to include in your boat a device which monitors their state of charge and gives a clearly visible signal when any of them falls below a pre-set

limit. For those batteries which are required to operate the diving tank the signal should be to empty the tank and refuse to flood it again. Failure to do this involves the danger that the battery might not have sufficient capacity to empty the diving cell against water pressure, and the boat would then fail to surface.

The heart of this circuit is the serial voltage regulator TL431, which is normally used as a highly stable variable Zener diode. If a voltage of more than 2.50V is present at its control input compared with the anode, then the cathode-anode path is left open. If the voltage falls below this value, then the regulator opens and the two transistors switch through after a delay of half a second. This action switches on the flashing diode and activates the relay; at the same time the control voltage falls so that the relay remains active even if the voltage should recover slightly. If the battery is deeply discharged it is not possible to ensure that the relay stays on, but by that time there should have been sufficient time to retrieve the model. The operator should already have been warned of the problem by the boat's refusal to surface, and by the flashing LED.

The relay contact is designed to influence the diving tank control system. For example, the relay could pull the input of the servo IC to + 4.8V so that the piston runs to its end-point or the emptying valve of a compressed air system is tripped.

Emergency buoy

Even the most perfect of model submarines may get caught on some invisible underwater obstacles, especially in a natural open-air pool. The spectrum of traps ranges from slime on the lake bed via tree roots, water plants and fishing lines to the occasional unseen dumped motorbike. If your boat gets comprehensively caught up in an obstacle, completely emptying the diving tank will often make no difference. Generally you will not even know where the accident has occurred, with the result that you end up searching with a rowing boat and a garden rake – for a good many hours.

If this should happen it is very helpful if your model is fitted with a small marker buoy which rises to the surface when you press a button on the transmitter. The buoy at least marks the position of the boat unambiguously. If the buoy's attachment cord is strong enough, a tug on it may even be sufficient to disentangle the model.

Many mechanisms for releasing the buoy can be dreamed up, and several have already been tried out. The simplest procedure is to stow the buoy in an opening in the boat and stick it there with a little invert sugar. The sugar slowly dissolves in the water and after about an hour the buoy rises to the surface. The time this takes should be slightly longer than the projected maximum running time. If an underwater "incident" occurs, you need to have the patience to stay on land until you see this crucial sign of life from your boat once the hour has elapsed. This principle has the great advantage that it is truly independent of all other apparatus on the boat. Instead of the invert sugar (from your local confectioner) other sticky, water-soluble substances can be used; the experimentally minded modeller has a lot of scope here. Jamming the buoy in place with a large lump of sugar candy crystal is just one of the numerous possibilities.

In another variant on this theme the buoy is held

against the boat's hull by an electro-magnet powered by the main drive battery. The power circuit can be interrupted by radio control and by a mechanical timer which, like the invert sugar, trips after an hour or so. The problem with the sugar system is that the owner's nerves are in a poor state if he has to wait a long time for the buoy to release automatically after an accident. With this arrangement the operator can push a button to release the buoy at any time. If for any reason the radio control system should fail, there is always the timer as an emergency back-up system. If even that should fail, the buoy should eventually be released when the main drive battery is completely flat. Of course, other alarm circuits can be linked to the buoy too, although the drawback is that a false alarm could be tripped while the boat is still moving, in which case the buoy cord will inevitably do its best to wrap itself round the propeller. For the same reason any radio-controlled release system should have a built-in delay of several seconds, otherwise any little glitch could release the buoy.

The buoy can be stowed in a suitable recess in the deck or in the turret. Emergency buoys of this type are often carried on full-size vessels, in which case all you have to do is install a working miniature. An adequately large free flooding space must be available close by in which the cable drum can be accommodated.

Good results have been obtained with a length of fishing line wound up on a large drum. This is very light in weight but extremely strong. A large-diameter drum and free-moving bearings should ensure that the line unwinds freely, and this is important as quite a small buoy is then sufficient. A good starting point is a 10cm≥ buoy (20mm diameter x 30mm) made of balsa wood with a waterproof paint finish, or a hollow plastic vessel.

Buoys are fitted to about half of all model submarines and offer reliable protection against the model's total loss.

Water alarm

Water alarms are available as standard commercial items, and they are often installed in model submarines, even though in my opinion they are relatively little use as a safety system. The residual buoyancy of a submarine is many times less than that of a surface vessel, so even a minor influx of water represents a major hazard. However, in most cases the electrodes of the water alarm cannot be installed at the lowest point of the bilges, so the alarm will be triggered very late. The same applies if there are several points at which water might collect.

A water alarm also gives the modeller a deceptive feeling of security; it can lead to a lack of conscientiousness in dealing with possible leaks. There are two very good reasons why model submarines should be completely watertight: on the one hand the on-board electronics will not tolerate moisture, and on the other the boat is extremely sensitive to weight changes when submerged. A regular check that the hull is truly watertight, using the excess pressure method as described earlier, is much more reliable in so far as it is a preventative measure, and it makes a water alarm superfluous.

Emergency surfacing systems

An emergency surfacing system is designed to produce a high level of upthrust in an emergency, e.g. water penetration or the onset of major manoeuvring incapacity. The idea is that the system will convey the submarine to the surface under any circumstances. Two different principles can be applied:

In research submarines the ballast or batteries can be jettisoned, with the result that the pressure hull complete with crew and vital systems are recovered. In this case it is accepted that the relatively inexpensive parts will be abandoned. Some large submarines incorporate free flooding compartments fitted with chemical gas devices which can quickly release a large quantity of gas in an emergency. The gas fills the free flooding compartments, and the the resultant gigantic upthrust causes the boat to shoot to the surface like a cork.

Both methods can be adapted for model use. Jettisoning ballast under servo control presents no major problem. In this case it makes sense to fit a marker buoy to the ballast to aid its subsequent recovery.

For the second method a gas-producing unit is needed, and a suitable item is the self-inflating mechanism designed for automatic lifebelts. These are based on carbon dioxide cartridges which are opened mechanically. The standard release mechanism reacts with water, and

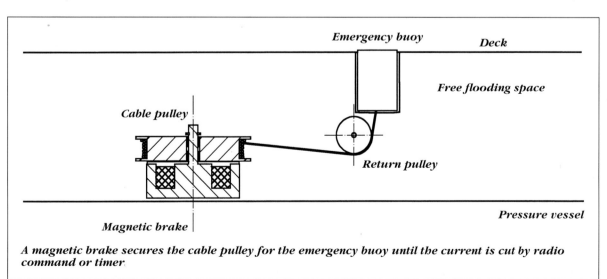

A magnetic brake secures the cable pulley for the emergency buoy until the current is cut by radio command or timer.

once this has been removed the mechanics can be used in the model. If your submarine does not have a free flooding compartment you can arrange for the gas to inflate a plastic bag.

It is easy to imagine how both methods could be installed in a model, but in practice I have never seen either of them used. The major problem seems to be the method of releasing the mechanism, which must be completely reliable and not prone to any form of interference.

Colour schemes

Colour is an important consideration in any discussion of safety measures. Military operators may not want their vessels to be seen, but we want quite the opposite. Scale camouflage schemes render any model submarine instantly invisible in an open-air pool once it has submerged; the camouflage is perfect.

Models of research submarines have a huge advantage here. These craft are usually painted in fluorescent colours which are visible at great distance even in quite murky waters. If you prefer military submarines you have to strike a compromise between scale camouflage colours and visibility, because an invisible boat is an accident waiting to happen. In many cases the modeller opts for a light shade of grey which looks "military" in character, but is still light enough to be picked out in the dark grey-green of the water. Bear in mind that this colour is hard to make out against the light blue of a swimming pool.

If you really want to apply the original colour scheme a useful idea is to install a reasonably powerful lamp (e.g. 10 W halogen) in the turret. This allows you to render your submarine visible just by pressing a button on the transmitter.

Chapter 11

Auxiliary Working Systems

Lighting systems

This auxiliary system is almost standard on model boats, and is just as easy to implement on a submarine as it is on a cruising ship. Sadly for all you modellers who love rows of lights, the number of lamps on a military submarine is a mere four or five – the minimum that any ship has to have as riding lights. The individual lamps are not very bright in any case, and the effect is reduced further by miniaturisation. Builders of research and fantasy submarines have things a lot better. They can fit a tiny lamp to every corner of the model without it looking wrong.

The miniature filament bulbs usually employed in other fields of modelling are often used on model subs, as are coloured light-emitting diodes (LEDs). These are usually attached to the turret or external parts so that the wiring is also exposed to the water. As a result they have to be very carefully insulated, otherwise the wires – the positive conductor, at least – would quickly be corroded away electrolytically under the influence of the voltage present.

Powerful lamps giving a sharp cone of light look extremely attractive under water, as the beam is shown up very well by the suspended particles which are always present in water. Halogen lamps rated at ten or twenty Watts can be run direct in the water, without their casing, and maintain their efficiency for quite a long time. They make excellent searchlights for research submarines. Perhaps with suitable optics a sharp beam of light could be arranged to shine out of a periscope; not scale, of course, but it should look effective.

Stroboscopic flashing lights are also fitted to research submarines, as they enable the boats to be seen at great range. They can do the same job on a model, since they remain visible when the boat itself has long since vanished in the dark green of the depths. The flashers then allow you to control the boat when you can't see it, and also to find it again if disaster should strike. Unfortunately the heavy currents which flow for very brief periods to supply the flash tubes are extremely powerful sources of interference to the radio control system. Since reception conditions in model submarines are so poor, the interference is greatly magnified, although the worst effects can be eliminated by keeping the flasher system and the receiving system well apart. Use a separate battery to prevent the problem of interference from the power supply leads.

Far less problematic is the use of a simple, powerful filament bulb controlled by an electronic pulse unit, even though such systems are far less bright. There is no high voltage system, so the problems associated with producing it are eliminated. If all you are concerned about is improved visibility in murky waters, then a 5 Watt lamp is adequately bright for continuous use.

Periscopes and snorkels

These are the most characteristic of all auxiliary functions on submarines, but working systems on model submarines are amazingly rare.

If your boat is fitted with a compressed air system it is a very simple matter to arrange an extending periscope. The system consists of no more than a long, thin double-acting cylinder whose piston rod forms the shaft of the periscope. If it is to reach the full extended height, it has to run from the turret right down into the bilges. As such it causes a major obstruction to the other internal fittings.

To control the system a 4-way valve is required. A cheap solution is to use two micro piston valves operated by one servo. To prevent the extension and retraction movements working too abruptly, chokes should be fitted in the cylinder hoses. Special throttle return valves are generally used for this, screwed directly into the cylinders, although a cheaper alternative would be to fit two compression throttles (aquarium fittings).

The exhausted air can be directed straight into the

Boat with lighting system

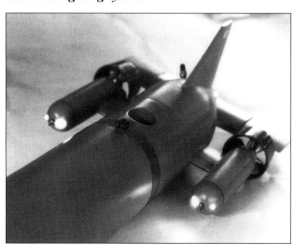

Periscope system on type XXI U-boat (L. Mentz)

powerful motor and extremely high spindle speed to achieve this. A better bet would be a rack and pinion or friction wheel/rod transmission system. The friction wheel system does not even need end-point switches, as it can slip if it jams and when it reaches the end-points.

If you opt for this method the drive motor has to be located in the free-flooding turret, and therefore has to be in a watertight enclosure. The low rotational speed means that the shaft can be sealed by a simple O-ring. Of course, the motor could be installed inside the pressure hull in which case the friction wheel would be driven via an angle gearbox.

A very simple method of operating an extending periscope would be a hydraulic system actuated by a gear-driven pump. The periscope then takes the form of a long, single-acting cylinder whose pressure cavity is pumped full of water by the geared pump. Minor leaks are not a major problem, so no seal is required at all. If the top end of the cylinder tube is located above the surface of the water, air is sucked in when the periscope is retracted (by reversing the pump), and this temporarily prevents the pump working. Once the sub is under water, however, the system vents itself automatically. This principle can be used to move telescopic cylinders of considerable length which still do not project inside the pressure hull.

hull, although this does raise the internal pressure considerably if the system is operated repeatedly under water. In this case it would be better to vent the air outboard via a non return valve.

However, the vast majority of modellers will be obliged to build a mechanical periscope actuator, since compressed air systems are not that common. This is not necessarily a drawback as these systems consume much less energy. Even in full-size subs the extending apparatus is usually powered by an electro-hydraulic system.

There are various possible methods of converting the rotary movement of the electric motor into the linear movement of the periscope – just as there are with the piston tank. With the time scale in mind, the extension should take place over a period of about one second. The low efficiency of spindle drive systems requires a

The drive system for the folding snorkel used on Type VII U-boats is often based on bevel gears and a geared motor located in the pressure hull. The idea of using an extending or folding snorkel for its original purpose, and venting the on-board compressor with it, is a challenge which to the best of my knowledge has not been taken up successfully to date.

Cameras

We despatch our model submarines into a world

which is out of our own reach, and never see anything of it. Of course we could train to be divers, but anyone can do that nowadays; perhaps we don't need to build submarines after all. However, people are large and usually keep breathing under water, and all this activity causes such turbulence that small things are simply washed away and all the mud is thrown up into blinding eddies. In contrast, a model submarine with large, slow-revving propellers hardly disturbs the water at all, and in principle allows us to observe things which would not be possible in any other way. Good examples are the photographs of the inside of the wreck of the "Titanic", lying at a depth of 3000m. They were taken by the radio-controlled "Jason Junior" mini-submarine, controlled from the "Alvin" from a location outside the wreck.

Many a modeller dreams of transmitting video from his submarine, but two obstructions have to be circumvented: Post Office regulations and the price of the equipment. It is not for me to say that you cannot possibly ignore the P.O. regulations which forbid radio transmission of the video signal – that is up to you; however, the transmitter you require is not that easy to obtain. Nor are suitable cameras exactly cheap to buy. It could be that technical developments will ease this situation in the near future, and I know of a number of modellers who are actually working on video-submarines at present.

Still cameras are a different matter, and many have been successfully fitted to model submarines. My modelling colleague Mr. Ganter has carried out many experiments in this field, and in his opinion the best camera for the job is a simple fixed-focus Instamatic devoid of any electronics. The automatic focusing systems of modern just-press-the-button cameras seem to be confused by the refraction which occurs under water, and all you obtain is blurred pictures. A good clear-view window would be a 10mm thick sheet of crystal glass fixed in place with silicone sealant.

Another possibility is to use a specialist waterproof still camera, of which a wide variety is available. One of these cameras can be installed as a temporary fitting on an ordinary model submarine. Most of them are watertight to a depth of at least 10m which is quite sufficient for our purpose. The focusing and light metering systems are specially designed for under-water use and present no problems. On large models they can simply be mounted on the deck, whereas on smaller boats suitable buoyancy vessels would have to be fitted to compensate for the additional weight.

Torpedoes

In their basic form torpedoes are independent, completely automated mini-submarines, armed with an explosive charge of considerable force. Considerable is also the word for the problems involved in producing a power system to the correct scale. At 1:50 scale a standard torpedo is the same size as a ball-point pen, and you would do well to install any form of drive system in one. More promising are the one-man and two-man miniature submarines, most of which are modelled to

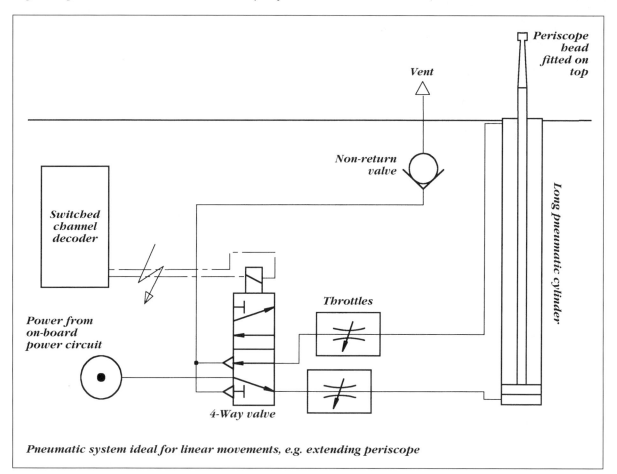

Pneumatic system ideal for linear movements, e.g. extending periscope

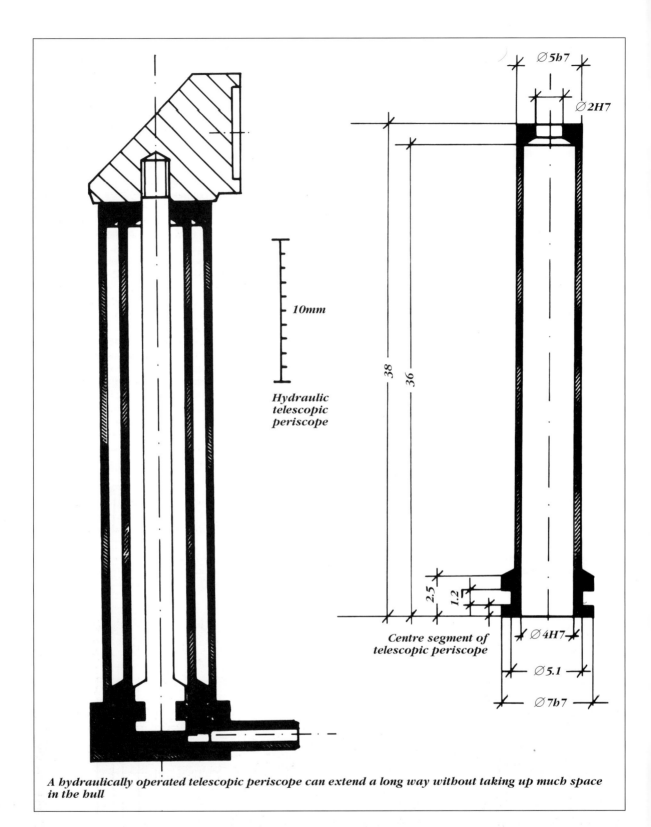

Ø5h7
Ø2H7
Ø4H7
Ø5.1
Ø7h7

38
36

2.5
1.2

10mm

**Hydraulic
telescopic
periscope**

**Centre segment of
telescopic periscope**

**A hydraulically operated telescopic periscope can extend a long way without taking up much space
in the hull**

large scales such as 1:10. In this case the torpedoes are a reasonable size, and a complete control system or even radio control system could be fitted.

Even though such a project might well represent an interesting exercise in technical sophistication, I consider it inappropriate to take such a highly sophisticated weapon of war as a prototype for a model. The primary

purpose of submarines – even military ones – is to provide under-water transport over long periods and distances, and these vessels can therefore be categorised principally as a means of travel. In contrast, torpedoes serve destructive purposes exclusively, and cannot be seen otherwise than as weapons. It is all too easy for children – in particular – to "play about" with such gruesome machines and thereby lose sight of their devastating intent and capability. I don't wish to be associated with that. Bear in mind also that you run the risk of being branded as a belligerent-minded person. I shall therefore not discuss the construction of model torpedoes any further.

Manipulators

Manipulators are the "hands" of the typical research submarine, and endow it with remarkable handling capabilities. These devices, with their six axes of movement, are not easy to use when the operator is some way away and standing on dry land, since the movements cannot be monitored accurately. Reducing the complexity to two or three axes of movement makes the whole business much easier to manage. Major movements can be carried out in any case by manoeuvring the whole boat. Adopting this principle also makes the apparatus much simpler in construction, to the point where it might well be possible to make one. Sensible movements would be extension, rotation and gripping. With a simplified system of this type it might well be possible to manipulate something under water, but unfortunately I know of nobody who has implemented this auxiliary function to date, so I can offer no proven suggestions for useful designs.

Unconventional drive systems

Most full-size submarines are fitted with straightforward battery-electric power systems which are proven and reliable, but many vessels have been tested with a variety of different energy sources. These include fuel cells, diesel engines in cyclical operation with oxygen,

This submarine is designed as a camera carrier, but at the time of this picture the equipment had not been installed

and what are known as water systems based on highly concentrated hydrogen peroxide. These installations are inevitably of complex construction and would absorb much development work for use in a model, not to mention their high operating costs.

One possibility is diesel-electric operation, as is "standard issue" on full-size subs. Recent years have seen the introduction of four-stroke glowplug engines which exhibit very docile running characteristics combined with low vibration, at least at low rotational speeds. On-board starters are also available, and this combination has already been used to implement power systems in many surface-running scale models. With the exception of their general working principle, these engines have almost nothing in common with the howling racing boat motors we still meet at the lakeside.

To date I have not heard of any installation of this type of system in a model submarine. In a large model

The owner of this research submarine, named "Alpenmolch", has already taken numerous photographs in mountain lakes

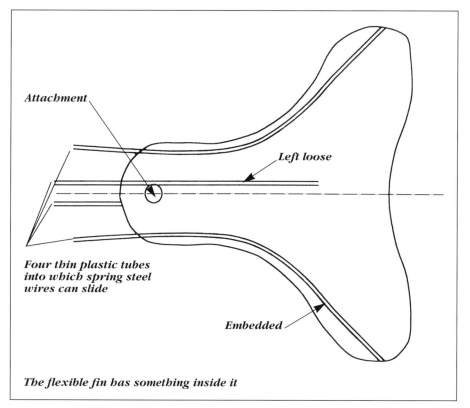

Attachment

Left loose

**Four thin plastic tubes
into which spring steel
wires can slide**

Embedded

The flexible fin has something inside it

Working fins

Most marine modelling is concerned only with miniature versions of full-size, man-made vessels, but if we leave that well-trodden path we soon come face to face with natural "submarines": fish, reptiles, mammals and insects. Whatever their method of propulsion, these creatures do not use rotating parts to make their way in life. Reproducing other forms of movement represents a wide and fascinating area for experimentation. To give you an idea of what is possible, the next section explains one attempt that has been made to reproduce the fin strokes of an ordinary fish.

The alternating movement of the tail fin is effected by an eccentric which drives the two-part tail section. The tail section constitutes about a quarter of the fish's total length and takes the form of a Becker rudder [a secondary rudder hinged to the primary rudder], to produce an approximation of even flexing. The silicone rubber tail fin proper is attached to this mechanism. The rubber element "gives" as it is moved sideways, and thereby produces forward thrust in a similar manner to an aircraft wing producing lift.

The "fish" is controlled using the pectoral fins – corresponding to the forward hydroplanes of an orthodox submarine – in conjunction with the dorsal fin. Thin plastic tubes are moulded into the edges of these fins to facilitate their movement. Spring steel wires can be slid in and out of the tubes by servo. The fin is stiffer if the wire is inside it, and the wire forces it to stand out at an angle, thereby producing a force in the vertical direction.

This gives a degree of depth control. For lateral control a similar system is used: plastic tubes of the same type (bowden cable inners) are located adjacent to the fin, and can be used to stiffen the fin on one side.

The lateral movement produced by the tail fin is then counteracted by increased resistance on one side, and a lateral control force (turn) is the result.

there should be plenty of space for a diesel generator, as it would be possible to reduce the battery capacity to make way for it. The generator would power the drive motors for surface running and at the same time charge the batteries. With this arrangement the internal combustion engine would not be connected to the propeller shaft at all, so the battery-operated drive system would require no modification. The generator could be a powerful electric motor, and this could also double as the starter motor.

The time does not seem to be ripe for a model submarine equipped with such a system; to be honest, most modellers are content if their submarine works at all, and have no time to spare to develop such a form of auxiliary working system.

For centuries model-makers have attempted to reproduce the movement processes of living creatures. In this case the beating tail fin of a fish is used as a means of propulsion in a radio-controlled model

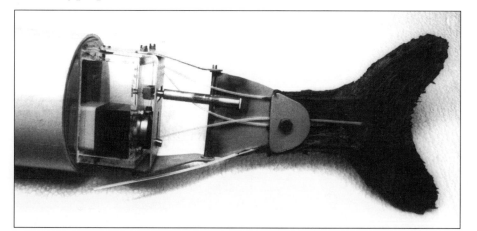

Bibliography

Lambert, John
H.M. Submarine Holland
P.O. BOX 35, Wolsey Road, Hemel Hempstead, Herts,
Great Britain.

Rössler, Eberhard
Geschichte des deutschen Ubootbaus
J.F. Lehmans Verlag, München. 1975

H.J. Lawrenz
Die Entstehungsgeschichte der Uboote
J.F. Lehmanns Verlag, München. 1968

Preston, Antony and J. Batchelor
Das U-boot seit 1919
W. Heyne Verlag. 1975

Gierschner, Norbert
Tauchboote
Transpress VEB Verlag für Verkehrswesen, Berlin (Ost).
1976

Dr. Ing. G Clauss
**Zur Dynamik schnell schwimmender Delfine, in:
Meerestechnik 1 (1970), Nr 4**

Andre Veenstra
Handbuch für Schiffsmodellbauer
Neckar-Verlag, villingen Schwenningen. 1978

Dubbel
Taschenbuch für den Maschinenbau
Springer-Verlag, Berlin, Heidelberg, New York.

Rob van Dort Joop Oegema
Handbuch Modell Dampfmaschinen Neckar-Verlag,
Villingen-Schwenningen. 1979

Appendix

Circuit board layouts

PARTS LIST FOR DIVING CELL SERVO ELECTRONICS

Quantity	Description	Value
1	IC1	NE 544
2	D1, D2	1N4148
1	T1	BC 549
1	T2	BC 517
2	T3, T10	BC 559
2	T4, T9	BD 435
2	T5, T7	BD 249C
2	T6, T8	BD 250C
2	R13, R19	100
2	R2, R1	10k
1	R7	18k
4	R11, R14, R18, R20	1k
4	R12, R6, R10, R17	220
2	R4, R5	2M2
1	R3	390k
2	R15, R16	47, 0.5 W
1	R8	68k
1	P3	5k Servo pot
2	P1, P2	10k Pot
4	C2, C6, C7, C11	100n
1	C9	1µ, Tantalum
2	C5, C10	220n
2	C3	2µ2, Tantalum
2	C4, C1	4µ7, Tantalum
2	K1, K2	End-point switches, circuit breakers. Eg: Micro-switches
1	S1	Servo plugs
1		Heat-sinks

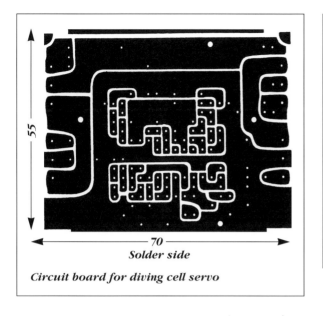

55

70
Solder side

Circuit board for diving cell servo

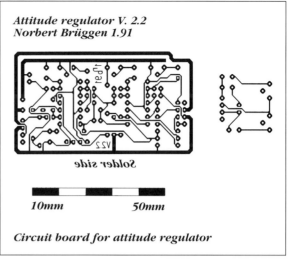

Attitude regulator V. 2.2
Norbert Brüggen 1.91

Solder side

10mm   50mm

Circuit board for attitude regulator

PARTS LIST FOR ATTITUDE REGULATOR

Quantity	Description	Value
2	IC1, IC2	NE556
1	IC3	CM 4001
2	D3, D2	1N4148
1	T1	BC556
3	R2, R3, R4	100k
1	R1	2.2Ohm
2	R6, R9	4k7
1	R5	10k
1	R7	68k (Possibly 47k)
1	R8	120k
3	R10, R11, R12	50k Trim pot, small, vertical Piher PT10h
2	C3, C5	1n Ceramic
1	C12	2.2nF Ceramic
6	C4, C6, C8, C9, C10, C11	10n Ceramic
1	C1	47μ, Tantalum 16V
1	C2	μ47, Tantalum 16V
1	C7	47n Ceramic
1	S2	Servo socket
1	S3	3-Pin plug
1	S1	Servo plug

Optical Inclinometer:

1	D1	LED 5mm Red
2	T2, T3	BPY 99
1	R13	470Ohm
2	R14, R15	1k

PARTS LIST FOR DEPTH REGULATOR

Quantity	Description	Value
1	U5	Inclinometer measuring chamber
1	U4	KPY 43A
		Improved replacement for KPY 10
1	IC6	4805
1	IC3	74HC4066
1	IC2	4098
1	IC1	TL064
4	D7, D5, D6, D8	1N4148
2	D4, D3	LED Red
		Caution: Only use dark LED with Ud<1.5V
		Not a high efficiency type
2	D1, D2	LED Green
1	T1	BC 546
3	R23, R11, R29	100k
1	R19	10M
4	R6, R7, R13, R27	10k
2	R24, R18	1M
2	R14, R15	1k
2	R26, R25	220k
1	R28	2M2
2	R3, R1	2k2
3	R2, R4, R5	33k
3	R8, R9, R10	470
2	R12, R30	47k
1	R22	4M7
3	R16, R17, R21	50k Trim pot PT10H
1	R31	1M Trim pot PT10H
1	R20	10k Spindle pot 64W
2	C3, C12	100n
3	C2, C9, C11	10n
1	C1	22n
1	C14	3n3
1	C10	470p
1	C4	10n MKS2
1	C6	47n MKS2
1	C5	100n MKS2
2	C7, C8	4u7 Tantalum 16V
1	C13=C*	u47 MKS2
1	C15	u47 Tantalum 16V
1	S1	5 Pin terminal
1	Inclinometer base	8 Pin terminal
1		Matching socket
2	Sockets	DIL14
1	Sockets	DIL16
1	Sockets	Round 8 pin or individual contacts

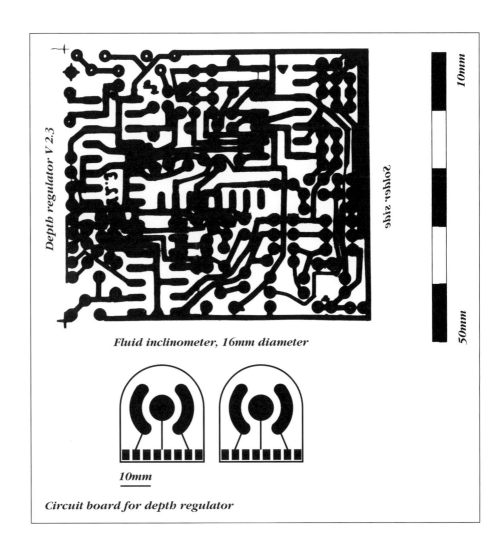

Depth regulator V 2.3

Solder side

10mm

50mm

Fluid inclinometer, 16mm diameter

10mm

Circuit board for depth regulator

CHANNEL DIMENSIONS FOR O-RINGS (IN MM):

O-Ring Axial Radial	Cross Section (For Static Scale)		(For Axial Movement)	
	B	T	B	T
1.0	1.3	0.75	1.2	0.90
1.5	1.9	1.1	1.9	1.35
2.0	2.6	1.5	2.4	1.8
2.5	3.2	1.9	3.0	2.25
3.0	3.9	2.3	3.6	2.75
4.0	5.2	3.15	4.8	3.7
5.0	6.5	4.0	6.0	4.65
6.0	7.8	4.95	7.2	5.65

Notes

Notes

Notes

Notes

Other Titles

INTRODUCTION TO MARINE MODELLING BY JOHN DAVIES & CHRIS JACKSON

£9.95 plus p&p

New to marine modelling? Then this title will start you off in the right direction, no matter which type of radio controlled boat you want to build. Each section looks at a different facet of this varied hobby, from powerboats to steam, scale electric to scale sail, offering expert advice on choice of model, power and radio requirements.

STATIC MARINE MODELLING BY PHILIP HYPHER

£12.95 plus p&p

In this book, the author describes his techniques for making a Venetian gondola, the P&O liner Maloja, the Oseberg Viking Ship and the famous Cunarder Aquitania. Preceding each model making chapter there is a section about the real boat or ship, giving a brief yet interesting insight into its historical background, and recommends research as being a most rewarding part of this fascinating hobby.

FAST I/C POWERBOATS BY TONY JARVIS

£9.95 plus p&p

This book offers a comprehensive introduction to the basic construction and racing principles of internal combustion (I/C) model power boats. It provides guidance on choosing, building and running I/C powered boats to suit the individual's preference and budget, and to suit UK and European competition rules and courses; with tips on the maintenance and repair of hulls, engines and radio equipment.

FAST ELECTRIC POWERBOATS BY PAUL WILLIAMS

£9.95 plus p&p

Advances in the technology of electric power have made electric powered model powerboats very exciting to build and run. Convenient in size and 'clean and green', they can be used in many smaller venues not suitable for I/C powerboats. Paul Williams, a top designer and competitor, has written this guide for the benefit of both newcomers and experienced modellers alike. Design considerations, building methods, choice of motors, speed controllers and batteries are all covered, as are tips on trimming for best performance and competition requirements.

Traplet Publications Ltd.,
Traplet House, Severn Drive,
Upton-upon-Severn,
Worcestershire,
WR8 0JL, England

Tel: +44 (0) 1684 594505 Fax: +44 (0) 1684 594586
E-mail: traplet@dial.pipex.com
Web Site: http://www.traplet.co.uk/traplet/